MW00625553

The Big Bang Revolutionaries

THE BIG BANG REVOLUTIONARIES

THE UNTOLD STORY OF THREE SCIENTISTS WHO REENCHANTED COSMOLOGY

JEAN-PIERRE LUMINET

SEATTLE   DISCOVERY INSTITUTE PRESS   2024

Description

Many widely read scientific writers of our day mistakenly attribute the concepts of the expanding universe and the Big Bang to Edwin Hubble and Albert Einstein. Hubble did provide evidence of an expanding universe, but he neither discovered such evidence nor accepted the radical idea that space itself was expanding. As for Einstein, he held out against the idea of an expanding universe for more than a decade, and ceased working in the field as soon as he had to amend his view. The real heroes of the Big Bang revolution are the Russian Alexander Friedmann and Belgian priest Georges Lemaître. That they are virtually unknown to the general public is one thing. That their contribution is underestimated by astrophysicists and cosmologists is another, for the concepts they promulgated are among the most remarkable achievements of twentieth-century science. *The Big Bang Revolutionaries* amends the record, telling the remarkable story of how these two men, joined by the mischievous George Gamow and in the face of conventional scientific wisdom, offered a compelling view of a singular creation of the universe in what Lemaître termed a "primeval atom."

Copyright Notice

© 2024 by Discovery Institute. All Rights Reserved.

Library Cataloging Data

The Big Bang Revolutionaries: The Untold Story of Three Scientists Who Reenchanted Cosmology
by Jean-Pierre Luminet
254 pages, 6 x 9 inches
Library of Congress Control Number: 2024934012
ISBN: 978-1-63712-040-8 (Paperback), 978-1-63712-042-2 (Kindle), 978-1-63712-041-5 (EPUB)
BISAC: SCI034000 SCIENCE / History
BISAC: SCI015000 SCIENCE / Space Science / Cosmology
BISAC: SCI005000 SCIENCE / Physics / Astrophysics

Publisher Information

Discovery Institute Press, 208 Columbia Street, Seattle, WA 98104
Internet: http://www.discoveryinstitutepress.com/
Published in the United States of America on acid-free paper.
First Edition, April 2024

ADVANCE PRAISE

"This excellent and well-illustrated book convincingly puts into a clear focus the key original contributions of Friedmann and Lemaître in the early twentieth-century revolution in our understanding of the large-scale physical universe."
—**Roger Penrose**, Emeritus Rouse Ball Professor of Mathematics at the Mathematical Institute of the University of Oxford, Emeritus Fellow of Wadham College at Oxford, Fellow of the Royal Society, and recipient of the Wolf Prize (1988) and the Nobel Prize in Physics (2020)

"The author brings together many aspects of thinking about the large-scale nature of our world from the points of view of concepts, theory, observation, and culture. The account starts with Albert Einstein's thought that a philosophically satisfactory universe has no boundary, a bold conjecture that proved to fit well with Einstein's new gravity theory and now agrees with the observational evidence. You will find fascinating details of the evolution of ideas, evidence, and the cultural situation between that time and the early steps by which George Gamow's brilliant intuition took him to the realization that an even better picture of our universe is that it expanded from a hot dense state."
—**Jim Peebles**, the Albert Einstein Professor in Science, emeritus, Princeton University, and recipient of the 2019 Nobel Prize in Physics

"It is rare to find an internationally distinguished astrophysicist who is also a searching and meticulous historian. It is rarer still to find such a person who is also a gifted prose stylist. Jean-Pierre Luminet is such a man. *The Big Bang Revolutionaries* is invaluable reading for anyone fascinated by the history of the big ideas that have shaped and reshaped Western science and civilization, and for anyone who wants a front row seat to witness the all-too-common character of scientific revolution—messy, full of unexpected twists and turns, and not without its casualties. In the present case and as Luminet dramatically shows, the revolution occurred in the face of sustained prejudice from some of the finest minds in physics and astronomy. As for the wider implications of the Big Bang revolution, Luminet leaves those for the reader to contemplate."

—**Stephen C. Meyer**, Director of the Center for Science and Culture and author of *Signature in the Cell*, named a Book of the Year by the Times (of London) Literary Supplement, *Return of the God Hypothesis*, and the New York Times bestseller *Darwin's Doubt*

"The twentieth century represents an exceptional period in the study of the cosmos. But this century will be remembered above all as the one in which physics, for the first time, made it possible to study the universe and its evolution. Jean-Pierre Luminet, an eminent cosmologist, takes the role of historian in this analysis of the emergence of ideas, and pays tribute to the physicists who contributed to this dizzying scientific adventure."

—**Michael Mayor**, Swiss astrophysicist and Professor Emeritus at the University of Geneva; a recipient of the Viktor Ambartsumian International Prize (2010), the Kyoto Prize (2015), and the Nobel Prize in Physics (2019)

"An inspiring overview of the history and physics of our modern view of the universe by the brilliant scientist Jean-Pierre Luminet, who was first to simulate black hole silhouettes. The reader is introduced to the scientific insights that revolutionized the perception of our cosmic roots and future. A fascinating read!"

—**Abraham (Avi) Loeb**, Frank B. Baird Jr. Professor of Science and Director of the Institute for Theory & Computation, Harvard University, and Director for the Breakthrough Initiatives of the Breakthrough Prize Foundation

"This book is a very careful discussion of the work of three less-known key figures who laid the foundations of modern cosmology—Alexander Friedmann, Georges Lemaître, and George Gamow. It does a great service in detailing the contributions that each of them made to the topic. I particularly appreciate the discussion of the pioneering work and personality of Lemaître, who can justly be called the father of scientific cosmology. With its discussion also of cosmic topology, the book is a unique contribution to the history of cosmology."
—**George Ellis**, Emeritus Distinguished Professor, University of Cape Town, co-author with Stephen Hawking of *The Large Scale Structure of Space-Time*, former president of the International Society on General Relativity and Gravitation, Fellow of the Royal Society, recipient of the Templeton Prize and the Georges Lemaître International Prize

"*The Big Bang Revolutionaries* is one terrific book. And one, I might add, of historical importance inasmuch as it restores to their rightful place two fascinating figures whom the standard history of physics in the twentieth century has shamefully neglected. Lucid? Of course it is lucid. Luminet is a fine astrophysicist. Moving? Very much so, not only for what it says about Friedmann and Lemaître, but for what it reveals about the author's sensitive intelligence on encountering the story of men whose position of prominence was denied them. It is, all in all, a splendid restoration—something very French, I might add, in that it describes men who should have been monarchs reacquiring their thrones."
—**David Berlinski**, Senior Fellow of the Center for Science and Culture, and author of *A Tour of the Calculus, The Advent of the Algorithm, Newton's Gift, The Devil's Delusion: Atheism and Its Scientific Pretensions*, and *Science After Babel*

"Finally a book that brings the credit of the great cosmological revolution of the twentieth century to where it is properly due: the Russian Alexander Friedmann and the Belgian priest Georges Lemaître."
—**Carlo Rovelli**, founder of the quantum gravity group of the Centre de Physique Théorique (CPT), Aix-Marseille University, and author of the bestselling *Seven Brief Lessons on Physics*

"Big Bang theory has become a popular topic, but who knows the scientists who first proposed the outrageous concept that our entire universe started as an ultra-dense fireball? Theoretical physicist Jean-Pierre Luminet, well-known for his pioneering work on the visualization of black holes, takes the reader through a pedagogical, and historically accurate, tour of the conceptual vistas opened by the inventors of Big Bang theory, namely: the Russian mathematician (and meteorologist) Alexander Friedmann, the Belgian cosmologist (and priest) Georges Lemaître, and, last but not least, the eclectic genius physicist George Gamow. A must-read for any person eager to understand one of the major scientific breakthroughs of twentieth-century physics."

—**Thibault Damour,** Institut des Hautes Études Scientifiques, recipient of the Einstein medal, the Galileo Galilei medal, and the Balzan prize

CONTENTS

1. A COSMOLOGICAL CRISIS (1925–1935)

We've got to live, no matter how many skies have fallen.
—D. H. LAWRENCE, *LADY CHATTERLEY'S LOVER* (1928)

So WROTE LAWRENCE IN THE FIRST PARAGRAPH OF HIS NOVEL, summarizing what he called the "position" of his heroine, and what he took to be that of the Western world more broadly, in the years following the devastation of World War I. The statement captures well two events that took place between 1925 and 1935, when the skies seemed to fall in both an economic crisis and a cosmological crisis. Both were unpredicted, and both, in their different ways, were brutal. In retrospect, there were a few hints of the coming crises, but the significance of these went undetected.

An economic crisis: in October 1929, after a long period of prosperity, the American stock market experienced a spectacular collapse. The economic and industrial situation worsened rapidly, and the crisis spread to other industrialized countries. Seeing their financial world dissolve overnight, dozens of businessmen took their own lives. Millions of people were put out of work. It would take nearly a decade to redress the situation.

Not as dramatic and affecting only the small world of theoretical physicists and advanced astronomers, the crisis in cosmology was roughly simultaneous with the events that began with Wall Street's Great Crash. It was what philosopher of science Thomas Kuhn called a *scientific revolution*.[1] A scientific revolution occurs when a widely held picture of the universe undergoes a fundamental transformation. Kuhn observed that, as time goes by, some scientific theories come to be regarded as secure and, consequently, are no longer subject to rigorous scrutiny. Accepted as a whole, each such theory comes to constitute a *paradigm*, namely a doctrine backed by consensus. The sciences, for this reason, rarely experience revolutions. Every scientific field—e.g., biology, chemistry, cosmology—reflects a specific corpus of knowledge accumulated over many years of observation, documentation, and experimentation. This corpus resists change.

Cosmological Paradigm Shifts

In the field of cosmology, it is generally admitted that our picture of the universe has undergone just three fundamental paradigm shifts: the Copernican-Galilean, the Newtonian, and the Einsteinian revolutions.[2] Today, it is possible that we are living through what will be recognized someday as a fourth cosmological revolution, with the appearance of new theoretical models based on quantum gravity. However, in the absence of experimental verification and formal completeness, none of the new approaches (superstring theory, loop quantum gravity, non-commutative geometry, emergent gravity, etc.) is guaranteed to be successful. Only time will tell if a fourth cosmological revolution is in the making.[3]

To better understand how scientific paradigms shift, let's look briefly at the Copernican-Galilean revolution. In 1543, Nicolaus Copernicus published *De Revolutionibus Orbium Coelestium*,[4] in which he promoted the heliocentric theory, an alternative model of the universe to Ptolemy's geocentric system. In 1572, a new star appeared in the constellation of Cassiopeia. Meticulously observed by the Danish astronomer Tycho Brahe, it cast doubt on the Aristotelian dogma of the immutability of the stars.[5] In 1600, Giordano Bruno was condemned by the Inquisition for having affirmed the infinity of space, the plurality of inhabited worlds, and other ideas considered theological heresies.[6] In 1609, Johannes Kepler, having analyzed Tycho Brahe's planetary data, had to abandon the paradigm of circular perfection, and described planetary trajectories in terms of ellipses.[7] Finally, in 1610, Galileo Galilei pointed a magnifying telescope towards the sky.[8] He revealed for the first time the imperfection of the moon, studded with craters, and of the sun, covered with spots. These observations opened the way to a unified terrestrial and celestial physics. The cosmological revolution, spread over nearly a century, thus saw the fall of the closed Aristotelian-Christian cosmos, centered on the Earth, in favor of an enlarged, perhaps even infinite space in which the Earth occupies only a marginal place.

Scientific revolutions often seem to accompany social, political, or economic revolutions. Perhaps it takes a great upheaval in society for scientists to dare to rethink their inherited world picture. Conversely, a change of scientific paradigm generates, in a subtler and slower way, new thoughts in other fields, including philosophy and aesthetics.[9] Thus, establishing the central position of the sun contributed to minimizing the importance of earthly or human affairs. This development could not leave philosophical and literary thought untouched.

Recasting Physics

If cosmological revolutions have so much cultural influence, it is because they recast fundamental physics. The Copernican-Galilean revolution led to the idea of unifying terrestrial and celestial physics, to the laws of planetary motion, and to the birth of mechanics. The Newtonian cosmological revolution, with its absolute infinite space and eternal time, within which the celestial bodies move subject to universal attraction, accompanied the statement of the fundamental principles of dynamics and the definition of forces. The Einsteinian cosmological revolution was marked by the discovery of the expansion of the universe and the recognition that the cosmos emerged from a possible singular origin, now called the "Big Bang."

This latter paradigm shift, known as relativistic cosmology, had as its source the theory of general relativity, whose field equations were given by Albert Einstein and David Hilbert in 1915. The theory essentially reworks the concepts of space, time, light, and gravitation. In its current version, relativistic cosmology also rests, as the Belgian physicist and Catholic priest Georges Lemaître predicted as early as 1931, on the other great pillar of modern physics: quantum mechanics, which, by describing the interactions between elementary particles and electromagnetic waves, reshuffles the concepts of classical mechanics.

Thus, the unfailing link between cosmology and fundamental physics does not facilitate the rapid assimilation of new cosmological paradigms. As far as the relativistic cosmological revolution is concerned, it took at least thirty years for a consensus—not unanimity—to begin to emerge among physicists.

To effectively advance knowledge, scientific revolutions typically are followed by times of recasting, which allow for purification, provisional stabilization, and the reformulation of new theories. However, the image that cosmology offers today of the evolution of the universe is remarkably close, in its fundamental concepts, to the models initially proposed by the Russian physicist Alexander Friedmann and, especially, by Georges Lemaître.

Relativistic Cosmology

The origin of the great cosmic structures has been found in the density inhomogeneities of the early universe. Traces of these irregularities were first detected in 1992 by the COBE (COsmic Background Explorer) observation satellite. In 1998, an era of high-precision observational cosmology began, which made it possible to fix the values of the fundamental parameters of the universe with small error bars. Analyzed between 2003 and 2012, data from the Wilkinson Microwave Anisotropy Probe (WMAP) satellite[10] on temperature fluctuations in the cosmic microwave background corroborated the generic Big Bang models, and made it possible to measure the essential characteristics (age of the universe, time dynamics, spatial geometry, energy contents) with remarkable accuracy. The European space telescope Planck, which operated between 2009 and 2012, further refined the measurements obtained by its American predecessor.[11] The interpretation of the successive data sets, delivered from 2013 to 2018, further reduced the experimental uncertainty regarding the parameters of the standard cosmological model.

Meanwhile, some of Lemaître's intuitions, long neglected, if not forgotten, have proved to be right—for example, the fundamental role played by quantum vacuum energy, both in the process of the birth of the universe and in the phase of accelerated expansion that currently seems to prevail. There is now little doubt about the relevance of the theory and observations on which relativistic cosmological models are based, even if, here and there, sound criticisms—though too quickly relayed and amplified by the popular media—still appear in the specialized literature.

Like the two previous cosmological revolutions, the relativistic revolution goes far beyond a strict astronomical context. Indeed, it is perhaps the most ambitious scientific theory in history. As philosopher Jacques Merleau-Ponty pointed out, it irreversibly transgresses the commandment of the reductionist catechism, "Thou shalt not speak of the Whole."[12] Relativistic cosmology is unique in speaking of the universe in its entirety. It may be for this reason that cosmology, although a very specialized discipline of physics, is the subject of constant comment and criticism by researchers outside the field.[13]

The True Fathers of the Big Bang

The purpose of this book is not to exhaustively survey the history of cosmology through the centuries, nor that of the few decades that saw the development of relativistic cosmology. The available studies on the subject are numerous, and some are of high quality.[14] I propose instead to present and analyze the texts that originated the three main ideas of relativistic cosmology:

- the expansion of the universe
- a possible singular origin of the universe
- the existence of a cosmic background radiation, a fossil memory of the origin

These texts are the work of three pioneers who, armed only with their "pens" and brilliant intuition, unveiled this new vision of the world: Alexander Friedmann[15] (1888–1925) and Georges Lemaître (1894–1966), both mentioned already, and the Russian-American George Gamow (1904–1968). At least three of their texts, the first published in 1922, the second in 1931, and the third in 1948, make them the real "fathers" of the Big Bang.

One of the anomalies of recent scientific history is that in the minds, and under the pen, of many widely read scientific writers, the concepts of the expanding universe and the Big Bang are attributed to two other, very famous, men of science: Edwin Hubble (1889–1953) and Albert Einstein (1879–1955). However, although Hubble did indeed experimentally demonstrate the linear relation between the spectral redshift of galaxies and their distance from us, he neither discovered such systematic spectral shifts (the discovery goes back to the American Vesto Slipher), nor did he accept the relativistic interpretation of his observations, i.e., the expansion of space itself instead of the mere motion of galaxies (more on this in Chapter 9).

Figure 1.1.

American astronomer Edwin Hubble in 1931. In 1929 Hubble published the first diagram suggesting that a galaxy's recessional velocity increases the farther it is from Earth, a relation dubbed Hubble's law but rebranded the Hubble–Lemaître law ninety years later. It was left not to Hubble but to others to formulate the idea, now the accepted view, that space itself is expanding (rather than galaxies receding) and that such an expansion could have started a finite time ago, a moment later called the "Big Bang."

As for Einstein, the inventor of the theory of relativity, we will see how he rejected for more than ten years the idea of an expanding universe—apparently on the basis of philosophical prejudices. And he stopped working in the field as soon as, faced with observational evidence, he had to amend his opinion.

That Friedmann and Lemaître are virtually unknown to the general public is one thing. The underestimation of their scientific contribution by the community of physicists, and even by astrophysicists and cosmologists, is another. It is very surprising if one considers that the concepts they promulgated will remain among the most remarkable achievements of twentieth-century science. Yet the *Biographical Encyclopedia of Scientists*[16] grants only short notices to Friedmann and Lemaître; the French dictionary *Inventeurs et Scientifiques*[17] quotes Lemaître but not Friedmann; and although the most serious and complete compilation of this type, the *Dictionary of Scientific Biography*,[18] devotes an article to each, the development is more than modest in view of the scope of their work. Gamow is better off. He is widely quoted in all the above-mentioned works, and even some of the general public know his name thanks to the popular books he wrote (translated into many languages).

To be sure, Friedmann and Lemaître receive some recognition outside the encyclopedias and specialized dictionaries. In Anglo-American literature, Friedmann's name is attached to the generic Big Bang models—most often alongside those of Howard P. Robertson and Arthur G. Walker in the so-called "FRW models." Lemaître's name is the least familiar of the three, although the term "FLRW models" is increasingly used. Indeed, a Georges Lemaître International Cosmology Prize was created in 1997, of which the 2019 Nobel Prize-winning physicist P. J. E. Peebles was the first recipient (and the present author the third recipient). And in 2018, the members of the International Astronomical Union voted to recommend renaming the Hubble law as the Hubble-Lemaître law (see Chapter 9). Notwithstanding all this, the respective reputations of Lemaître, Friedmann, and Gamow are inversely proportional to the importance of their cosmological work.

There are many possible reasons for this situation. Some might point to the language barrier. Friedmann published his works in

German or Russian, and most of Lemaître's articles were written in French. However, Einstein and the French physicist and mathematician Henri Poincaré, to name but two examples, also expressed their fundamental results in their native language, and they are no less recognized because of that.[19]

Perhaps of greater relevance, Friedmann and Lemaître do not belong to the "Anglo-American Empire," a fact that today constitutes a serious handicap in gaining international scientific recognition, whether in life or posthumously. (Gamow settled in the United States in 1934.)

Certainly, too, the historical record can be distorted by this or that influential chronicler. For instance, an article on relativistic cosmology published by American physicist Howard Robertson in 1933, while otherwise excellent, was misleading about the contemporary history it described.[20] In suggesting that the concept of an expanding universe was already accepted, it reflected more the secret wish of its author than a historical objectivity.

As for the particularly acute neglect of Lemaître, note that Soviet authors such as Friedmann and Gamow have been the object of more attention from American scientists than French-speaking authors such Lemaître have been. A first and obvious reason is that Soviet scientific production was much greater than that of French-speaking scientists. But political and ideological motives also played a role. From the advent of Soviet communism, which threatened the values of American capitalism, and even more so during the Cold War period, American researchers paid particular attention to the work of their adversaries. Moreover, after the collapse of the Soviet regime, most of Russia's best physicists had to emigrate to continue working in their field, and the United States created positions capable of absorbing this sudden influx of high-level researchers.

In addition to these general reasons, there are specific reasons. Friedmann died prematurely, even before astronomical observations could support his thesis. Were it not for his early death, one wonders how far the Russian scientist would have pushed his investigations in relativistic cosmology. As far as Lemaître is concerned, even though he initiated the first two conceptual advances mentioned above, his specialty as a mathematician and his religious commitment undoubtedly crystallized professional resistance to him among physicists and astronomers.[21] As for Gamow, if his contributions to various scientific fields (nuclear physics, astrophysics, cosmology, and even genetics) are not recognized for their true value, it is, according to his closest collaborators, Ralph Alpher and Robert Herman, in some measure due to his irrepressible sense of humor and his very free and detached conception of life in general (and of science in particular), which have led many perhaps humorless scientists to take his research work less seriously than it deserves.

The situation is gradually changing. Friedmann and Lemaître are increasingly recognized as innovators in the lineage of Ptolemy, Copernicus, Kepler, Galileo, Newton, and Einstein. Biographies have been devoted to each of them. Among the current spokesmen for cosmology, some are beginning to recognize the founding roles played by Friedmann and Lemaître,[22] including through cosmology books that have enjoyed some popular success.[23]

Thus the respective contributions of the scientists who participated in the elaboration of the new cosmological paradigm are finally becoming clearer: Einstein created the theory of general relativity and wrote the field equations governing the physical and geometrical properties of the universe; Friedmann discovered the non-static solutions for these equations, describing the time variation of space, and glimpsed the universe's possible beginning in a singularity; Lemaître linked the theoretical concept of the expansion of space to the observed apparent motion of galaxies, laid the physical foundations of the Big Bang models, anticipated the fundamental role played by quantum mechanics and vacuum energy, and predicted a phase of accelerated expansion of the universe due to a kind of repulsive field of energy; Hubble proved the extragalactic nature of spiral nebulae and experimentally established the law of proportionality between their recession speed and their distance (which is only an approximation, valid at low redshift, as Lemaître first recognized). Gamow, finally, showed how light elements were formed in the early hot universe, and with his collaborators, Alpher and Herman, predicted the existence of the cosmic background radiation.

The Six Periods of Relativistic Cosmology

In the one hundred years of relativistic cosmology, we can distinguish six periods.

1. The *initial period* (1917–1927) sees the development of quantitative relativistic cosmological models, but the physical significance of these models, especially the relation with astronomical observations, is not understood.

2. The *period of development* (1927–1945) shows the intense exploration of geometrical and dynamical aspects of universe models, and the interpretation of spectral shifts as evidence of an expanding universe.

3. The *consolidation period* (1945–1965) corresponds to mathematical developments and improvements in observational data, ending with the discovery and interpretation of the cosmic microwave background radiation. Then begins:

4. The *period of acceptance* (1965–1980) of the "Big Bang" models,[24] which gave way to

5. The *period of enlargement* (1980–1998), when modifications, mostly from high energy physics, are made to the standard Big Bang models, even going as far as the introduction of more general geometries than the four-dimensional pseudo-Riemannian manifolds.

6. The *period of experimental renewal* (1998 to the present), where high-precision observations now make it possible to measure the values of the parameters of the universe to within a few percentage points, and where the problems of the cosmological constant, vacuum energy, and topology have been renewed.

The texts analyzed in this volume all relate to the first three periods. Those of Friedmann belong to the initial period, those of Lemaître to the development period, those of Gamow to the consolidation period.

It is, in fact, Lemaître's work that defines the divisions between the first three periods. His 1927 article inaugurates the development period, while his collection of articles, published in 1945 as *The Primeval Atom Hypothesis*, closes it.

2. GRAVITATION (4TH CENT. BC–1917)

A God who would suddenly want to destroy the worlds would only have to take away the attraction of matter. At that moment everything would dissolve into what we can no longer call space, since there would be no more space, since only the movements and displacements of matter create its existence.
—MAURICE MAETERLINCK, *THE GREAT LAW* (1933)

GRAVITATIONAL INTERACTION GOVERNS THE STRUCTURE OF THE universe on an astronomical scale, and the founding texts of modern cosmology would not have been written without the prior elaboration of general relativity, which is a theory of gravitation. The road to this understanding of gravity was neither brief nor straight. It seems useful to briefly recall that history here.[1]

Pre-Relativistic Theories

To begin with, Aristotle asserted that force could only be applied by contact—remote force being, according to him, impossible.[2] He further argued that a constant force was necessary to keep a body moving in a straight line. This obviously false notion (otherwise arrows shot from a bow would not fall according to a parabolic curve) impeded the understanding of gravity for two millennia.

Then came the new heliocentric system, proposed by Copernicus in 1543: The planets revolve around the sun, but what moves them? Copernicus did not answer that question, but in the decades that followed, the laws of planetary motion discovered by Kepler, and the laws governing the fall of bodies as described by Galileo, established a new framework for the development of a coherent theory of gravitation. This theory, known as universal attraction, was born in 1687 by the pen of Isaac Newton.[3]

After receiving their definitive analytical form, the laws of Newtonian gravitation were developed as very general and powerful methods, using new quantities related to force that are far from common experience, such as potential energy. The theory of universal attraction was only really accepted after experimental confirmations, such as the shape of the Earth (1736), the return of periodic comets (Halley's comet, 1759), and the discovery of new planets (Neptune, 1846).

Despite these practical triumphs, remote gravitational action remained unexplained. In an 1864 paper,[4] James Clerk Maxwell made some profound remarks on this subject, which he developed in his famous treatise of 1873.[5] Wishing to explain the electromagnetic action between distant bodies without assuming the existence of forces capable of acting at a distance, Maxwell hypothesized the existence of a field distributed throughout space. He noted that, having linked magnetic and electric attractions and repulsions to the action of a surrounding medium, and having found that they depend on the inverse of the square of the distance, it was natural to wonder whether gravitational attraction, which follows the same law of variation with distance, could not also be linked to the action of a medium. However, Maxwell admitted his inability to proceed with his investigations into the causes of gravitation.

At the dawn of the twentieth century, Hendrik Lorentz highlighted the variation of time and space intervals with the speed of the reference frame and gave the transformation formulas between two frames of reference with uniform relative speed, which would allow the development of special relativity.[6] He also conjectured that gravitation could be attributed to an interaction that was not instantaneous, but instead propagated at the speed of light.[7] In a June 1905 article, submitted a few days before Einstein's paper on the same subject, Henri Poincaré set out the principle of special relativity: all reference frames with uniform relative velocity are equivalent, the form of physical laws being invariant under the Lorentz transformations.[8] Noting, however, that the Newtonian law of gravitation does not meet this criterion, he proposed the existence of gravitational waves traveling at the speed of light, but did not develop any particular theory on the subject.

The Development of General Relativity (1907–1916)

In 1907, Einstein took up the problem of gravitation posed by Poincaré. How should Newtonian gravitation be modified to be compatible with special relativity? He suspected that the Equivalence Principle, i.e., the equality of inertial mass and gravitational mass observed experimentally, must play a key role in gravitation. Then came what he would later call "the happiest idea of [his] existence," namely that an observer in free fall would not feel any gravitational field: in other words, there is a complete physical equivalence between a gravitational field and a suitably accelerated reference system.

This hypothesis allowed him to generalize the principle of relativity to the case of uniformly accelerated motion, and showed that the basic postulate of special relativity is too narrow: to describe gravitation, one must also consider the equivalence between all reference systems in uniform relative acceleration, resulting in the independence of the form of physical laws with respect to certain non-linear transformations of coordinates in a four-dimensional space.

According to the Equivalence Principle, all forms of energy must be influenced by gravitation, including light. The German astronomer Erwin Finlay Freundlich convinced Einstein of the importance of astronomical observations to test gravitational theories, including the deflection of light in a gravitational field. Einstein had previously thought only of terrestrial experiments, leaving little chance of measurable results because of the weakness of the gravitational field involved. In a 1911 paper, Einstein also discussed the gravitational redshift, according to which light escaping from a massive star must be shifted to longer wavelengths, because of the loss of energy due to the gravitational field.[9]

In 1912, Einstein showed that Lorentz's transformations are incompatible with a non-Newtonian description of gravitation incorporating the Equivalence Principle. This research encouraged other physicists to build gravitational theories. Gunnar Nordström, Max Abraham, and Gustav Mie made various attempts, all inspired by Einstein's Equivalence Principle, according to which light is influenced by gravity, but failed to develop a satisfactory theory.[10]

Figure 2.1.

German Physicist Albert Einstein in 1904. The following year he would publish his special theory of relativity. In three years he would take up the problem of gravitation posed by Poincaré: How should Newtonian gravitation be modified to be compatible with special relativity?

For his part, Einstein understood the technical background of the problem: if all accelerated reference systems are equivalent, then euclidean geometry cannot be valid at every point in space. He then realized the fundamental physical importance of the foundations of geometry and, as a result, changed his mind about mathematics, which he had previously neglected somewhat. His friend Marcel Grossman set out to explain to him the recent mathematical developments on curved spaces obtained by Friedrich Bernhard Riemann, Gregorio Ricci, and Tullio Levi-Civita.[11] In 1913, Einstein and Grossman together signed an outline of a theory of general relativity and a theory of gravitation in a two-part article—a physical part written by Einstein and a mathematical part written by Grossman—in which the use of tensor calculus significantly advanced gravitational formalism.[12] Grossman provided Einstein with the Riemann-Christoffel curvature tensor, which would become the basic geometric tool of the future theory. For the first time, gravitation was described in terms of a metric tensor, whose coefficients play the role of gravitational potentials. However, the theory remained incorrect because their field equations did not satisfy the principle of covariance.

In June 1915, Einstein spent a week in Göttingen, where he gave six lectures on his version of general relativity. David Hilbert and Felix Klein attended these lectures and Einstein, after leaving Göttingen, expressed his satisfaction at having convinced them.

In October 1914, Einstein tried to solve the problem but in an erroneous way.[13] The last steps of the theory of general relativity were accomplished almost simultaneously by Einstein and Hilbert,[14] who both recognized the errors in Einstein's October 1914 article.

By November 1915, Einstein realized that his theory naturally explained the advance of the perihelion (the point in a planet's orbit where it is closest to the sun) of the planet Mercury. In 1859, the French astronomer Urbain Joseph Le Verrier had indeed noted that the perihelion advances over time, part of the advance being explained by the gravitational perturbations of the other planets, a residual part of 38" (arcseconds) per century remaining unexplained in terms of what was known at the time. Many possible solutions had been proposed in the context of Newtonian gravitation: for example, that the sun was very flattened, that Venus was 10 percent more massive than previously thought, or that another planet called Vulcan gravitated inside Mercury's orbit—hypotheses that were disproved by observations. There remained the possibility that Newton's law itself was incorrect. Since 1882, the advance of the perihelion was known with more precision: 43" per century, a value confirmed by Freundlich in 1913. In November 1915, Einstein thus applied his gravitational theory to the description of Mercury's orbit and discovered that the advance of 43" per century could be precisely explained within the framework of his new gravitational theory, without invoking the existence of invisible bodies or other ad hoc hypotheses. Einstein's article, dated November 18, did not yet present the correct form of the field equations, but this did not affect the calculation concerning Mercury's orbit.

Einstein also showed that the calculation of the deflection of light that he had presented in his 1911 work was wrong by a factor of 2, the correct value being 1"74. In fact, a German expedition had been planned during the summer of 1914 to the Crimea to test Einstein's 1911 prediction of 0"83. But Freundlich, the leader of the expedition—described by Einstein, in a letter to Paul Ehrenfest, as "my brave astronomer"—had been taken prisoner on the Russian front, and the expedition naturally stopped. Had these measurements been made, the value then proposed by Einstein would have been denied and this negative result would have cast a serious shadow on the value of his gravitational theory.

On November 25, 1915, Einstein submitted his fundamental article "The Equations of the Gravitational Field," fixing the correct form of general relativity.[15] The calculations of the deflection of light rays and the advance of Mercury's perihelion remained identical to those made a week earlier.

On November 20, Hilbert also submitted his paper, "*Grundlagen der Physik*," providing the correct equations of gravitation. He made key contributions to relativity absent from Einstein's work. He applied variational principles to gravitation and gave without demonstration a set of remarkable identities which he attributed to the female mathematician Emmy Noether.[16] Hilbert's article also expressed the hope for a geometric unification of gravitation and electromagnetism.

Immediately afterwards, Karl Schwarzschild discovered an exact mathematical solution of the equations, corresponding to the gravitational field created by a massive spherical body. This work, originally purely theoretical, was to remain misunderstood for a long time. It would become the touchstone for the understanding of neutron stars, pulsars, and black holes.

In 1916, Einstein published an article explaining the foundations of general relativity in more easily understandable terms.[17] All that was missing now was experimental verification.

Astronomers knew that in May 1919 they would have a chance of observing the deviation of light rays in the solar gravitational field during a perfect solar eclipse. The circumstances were particularly favorable for the experiment because the sun would occult in the foreground the stellar cluster Hyades, which is very rich in stars. Sir Frank Dyson, the astronomer royal, began preparations for the observation as early as 1917, organizing two simultaneous British expeditions, one to Sobral in northeastern Brazil, led by Andrew Crommelin, and the other to the island of Principe, off the coast of Portuguese Guinea, led by Arthur Eddington.

These expeditions set forth immediately after the armistice of 1918. And their observations were successful: by providing values of 1"98 ± 0"30 at Sobral and 1"61 ± 0"30 at Principe, the experimental data were consistent with Einstein's prediction. The theoretical field was now ready for cosmology.

3. Static Cosmologies (1917)

I have perpetrated something... in gravitation theory, which exposes
me a bit to the danger of being committed to a madhouse.
—Albert Einstein to Paul Ehrenfest (1917)[1]

The father of general relativity was the first to seek a
solution for the field equations applicable to the whole universe.
The era of relativistic cosmology began with the publication in 1917
of Einstein's article *"Kosmologische Betrachtungen zur allgemeinen
Relativitätstheorie"* ("Cosmological Considerations on the General
Theory of Relativity").[2]

Einstein's Motionless Universe

The link between gravitation and the structural properties of the
universe was one of Einstein's most brilliant ideas, but its genesis
went back to an earlier time, namely the publication of a famous
memoir by the German mathematician Friedrich Bernhard Riemann
(1828–1866).[3]

The transition from the theory of general relativity to physical
cosmology was, however, not obvious; it was necessary to assume
that Riemannian geometry applied in the universe on a large scale.
Einstein explained this later, in a lecture given in Berlin on January
27, 1921.[4] After showing how the use of Riemannian geometry—
which he called "practical geometry"—was essential for the description of the four-dimensional space-time metric, he wondered about
the validity of this geometric approach on both a small and a large
scale. For small scales, he noted that "the physical interpretation of

geometry presented here ceases to be valid when it is applied directly to domains of space of a sub-molecular order of magnitude." Einstein thus anticipated the difficulties he would encounter for the rest of his life—difficulties theorists still face today—in formulating a theory of quantum gravitation. But of large scales he said, "Less problematic appears the extension of the concepts of practical geometry to regions of space of a cosmic order of magnitude."

A static universe (in which the relative distance between two points does not vary over time) did not seem to be in doubt. Therefore, Einstein quite naturally hypothesized a homogeneous universe, filled with matter without pressure, of constant density in space and time. Uniform distribution of matter in space implies uniform curvature: the spatial part of Einstein's universe has a positive curvature, everywhere the same. It is therefore a space with a spherical geometry: if you send a light ray straight ahead and wait long enough, it comes back to you. Einstein's model has at least two merits. First, it demonstrates the technical efficiency of general relativity in tackling the cosmological problem; secondly, it shakes the belief in an infinite universe by proposing a finite but limitless space.

But if Einstein dared to touch space, he did not dare to touch time. Here lies the fatal flaw in his cosmological model: Einstein's universe is matter without motion. Many commentators later wrote that Einstein could not shake off a "cultural" and "philosophical" influence dating back to Aristotle, according to which the cosmos was immutable. It would be more appropriate to refer to Spinoza for Einstein's implicit philosophy. But fixating on either of these predecessors as the cause is to ignore some of the theoretical physicist's more pragmatic motivations.

Einstein indeed knew that stars have weak proper motions, and he assumed that there was no other large-scale secular motion. Observations at the time did not provide any clear contradictions to this hypothesis, and the extragalactic nature of spiral nebulae was not yet clear. It was therefore legitimate to consider the universe as a simple gas of stars, and Einstein reasoned as follows: if the universe is infinite in both space and time, as proposed by Newtonian cosmology, then

Figure 3.1.
Albert Einstein lecturing in Vienna, 1921.

to complete the equations of general relativity it is necessary to specify boundary conditions at infinity. However, Einstein retained an idea from the physicist and philosopher Ernst Mach (1838–1916),[5] according to which a single particle in a space empty of matter would have no inertia.

In 1872, Mach had indeed established the principle that only relative motion exists. According to him, centrifugal forces are produced when a body rotates relative to the fixed stars but not when the body rotates relative to another body and not to the fixed stars. Following him, Einstein believed that inertia was generated by the distribution of distant masses. However, gravitational potentials (the coefficients of the g_{ij} metric) are determined by the distribution of matter. For inertia to remain finite, the coefficients of the metric must cancel each other out at infinity; but since space does not exist without gravitation, this implies the pure and simple disappearance of space at infinity. This is the reason that Einstein abandoned the model of a spatially infinite universe and tried to find a solution to his equations describing a finite universe, filled with a static distribution of matter.

At this point he was disturbed by the Newtonian result that such an equilibrium is unstable at the slightest disturbance.[6] One of his arguments is particularly interesting because he used a form of reasoning related to statistical mechanics, a subject in which he was a master. Einstein envisioned the finite universe as a Boltzmann gas in equilibrium at some finite temperature, whose molecules are the stars. If the number of stars per unit volume must cancel at the border of the distribution, Einstein argued, it must also cancel at the center. Indeed, the ratio of the densities at the edge and at the center is equal to the ratio of Boltzmann's factors, $e^{-E/kT}$, involving the difference of the gravitational potentials at the two reference points.

However, this difference cannot be canceled, unless the density is zero everywhere. This contradicts the hypothesis that the average stellar density of the universe is a strictly positive constant. Einstein rightly deduced that general relativity, in its original formulation, was incompatible with a static universe.

The idea that non-static solutions could exist touched him, since, in his own words, "The curvature of space is variable in time and place, according to the distribution of matter."[7] However, he did not abandon the hypothesis of staticity, since he believed that observations (and not Aristotle's physics) required it. Consequently, he had no other choice but to modify the original formulation by introducing a *cosmological constant*, denoted by λ.

The only term that can be added to the field equations while respecting the covariance postulate is proportional to the metric tensor, the proportionality factor being the constant λ. If, formally, this new term can be incorporated into the stress-energy tensor, for Einstein it must be considered as having a different physical origin—not related to matter but to the very structure of space, hence its "cosmological" qualifier.

Having modified his equations, Einstein then set out to find a solution that would satisfy his hypotheses concerning the field and matter. He began by constructing a metric tensor. The conditions he set were that the time component is independent of space, that the metric tensor is diagonal, and that space has a constant curvature—the latter condition corresponding to the assumption of a uniform distribution of matter. To guarantee the finiteness of space, Einstein chose the simplest spatial geometry, that of the hypersphere of radius R, whose constant curvature is positive.

The resulting solution is known as Einstein's cylindrical universe. If we represent the direction of time by a vertical axis and draw a cylinder whose axis is along time, we obtain a projective description of Einstein's space in which two directions of space have been removed (Figure 3.2). The circle represents the perimeter of the spherical space at a given instant, and this perimeter does not vary over time. It is therefore a truly static space.

Equipped with this metric, Einstein could study the conditions for his equations that would admit such a static solution. There are two conditions, one linking the cosmological constant λ to the density of matter ρ, the other linking it to the radius of curvature of space R:

$$\lambda = 4\pi G\rho/c^2 = 1/R^2$$

Einstein's static model can be interpreted mathematically as the product of a hypersphere (reduced here to a grey circle of constant radius) by an infinite time axis. The light rays go around space in a so-called "circumnavigation" of time.

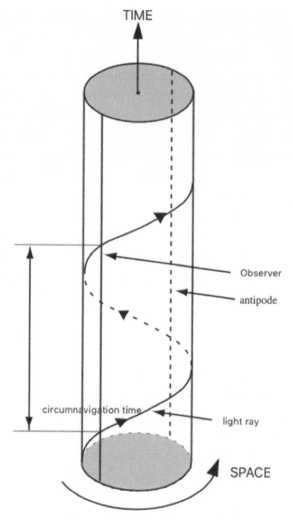

Figure 3.2.
Einstein's "cylindrical" universe.

With this inaugural article in modern cosmology, Einstein was aware that he was venturing into new territory. Indeed, he took the opposite side of the positivist philosophy illustrated by the German philosopher Immanuel Kant's assertion that "the representation of space cannot be obtained from the relations of outer appearance through experience."[8] Kant had believed that he had put an end forever to the debate on the finite or infinite character of space, by proving that it was impossible to construct without logical contradiction both a finite and an infinite universe, concluding that the question made no sense and that it was pointless to discuss it. This is precisely the idea Einstein's model defeated.

"Therefore the question whether the universe is spatially finite or not seems to me decidedly a pregnant question in the sense of practical geometry," Einstein said in his famous lecture "Geometry and Experience" before the Prussian Academy of Sciences, January 27, 1921. "I do not even consider it impossible that this question will be answered before long by astronomy."[9] And Einstein clearly took the side of a spatially finite universe, so as not to contradict Mach's principle:

> I must not fail to mention that a theoretical argument can be adduced in favour of the hypothesis of a finite universe. The general theory of relativity teaches that the inertia of a given body is greater as there are more ponderable masses in proximity to it; thus it seems very natural to reduce the total effect of inertia of a body to action and reaction between it and the other bodies in the universe, as indeed, ever since Newton's time, gravity has been completely reduced to action and reaction between bodies. From the equations of the general theory of relativity it can be deduced that this total reduction of inertia to reciprocal action between masses—as required by E Mach, for example—is possible only if the universe is spatially finite.[10]

On February 4, 1917, Einstein wrote to the Dutch physicist Paul Ehrenfest: "I have perpetrated something... in gravitation theory, which exposes me a bit to the danger of being committed to a madhouse."[11] Einstein could not suspect that in reality his cosmological model would soon prove to be timid, in view of the future work of Friedmann and Lemaître, which was nevertheless based on the same theory, general relativity.

De Sitter's Matterless Universe

Einstein commented regarding the cosmological constant "that the term is necessary only for the purpose of making possible a quasi-static distribution of matter, as required by the fact of the small velocities of the stars."[12] Despite this remark, the possible presence of a cosmological constant in the field equations can be considered independently of Einstein's specific static model. In the same year, 1917, the Dutch astronomer Willem de Sitter discovered a second cosmological solution to the equations of general relativity.[13]

De Sitter (1872–1934) first studied mathematics in Groningen, then switched to astronomy, working for three years at the Cape Town Observatory in South Africa. Starting in 1908, he held the chair of astronomy at the University of Leiden.[14]

He soon became interested in the possible implications of special relativity for astronomy. Thus, when in 1916 Einstein published his theory of general relativity, de Sitter was one of the first to grasp its importance. At that time, in the Netherlands, which remained neutral in World War I, de Sitter and his colleagues in Leiden were able to receive visits from Einstein. They were thus the first to have the

Figure 3.3.
Dutch astronomer Willem de Sitter.

opportunity to make his work known to the rest of the world. De Sitter sent Einstein's paper to Eddington, and himself published in 1916–1917 three articles in the *Monthly Notices*, which consisted partly of presentations of Einstein's work, and partly of his own investigations of the consequences of relativity for astronomy. He would go on to play an essential role in motivating astronomer royal Sir Frank Dyson to orchestrate the eclipse expeditions of 1919 to confirm the theory.

In de Sitter's third article he proposed an alternative to Einstein's cosmological model. It is still a static solution, in the sense that there is a coordinate system in which all the coefficients of the metric are independent of time, with a cosmological constant (if the latter is equal to zero, de Sitter's space is reduced to Poincaré-Minkowski's flat space, the unique solution of special relativity). De Sitter's solution differs from Einstein's in that it does not contain matter. More precisely, the forms of matter that fill de Sitter's universe, such as stars, are considered as "test particles" that do not generate gravitation. As such, they are in motion in a predetermined background metric. This obviously raises a conflict with Mach's principle, since no mass in the universe is likely to be responsible for local inertia. The question therefore arises: if no matter exists outside the test particle, does it possess inertia?

De Sitter's solution is represented by

$$\rho = 0, \lambda = 3/R^2$$

The three-dimensional spatial curvature R is positive (if λ is positive) and constant in time. De Sitter uses a coordinate system in which all components of the metric tensor cancel each other out when the distance to the origin of the coordinates tends towards infinity. In a postscript, de Sitter infers that the frequency of light vibrations decreases as the distance to the origin of the coordinates increases; consequently, the spectral lines of distant stars or nebulae must systematically be redshifted, giving rise to a "false" positive radial velocity—i.e., a recession speed. A negative radial velocity would denote instead a closer approach to the source and, by virtue of the Doppler effect, result in a spectral blueshift. De Sitter even alludes to "meager" observational clues, suggesting that such an effect has already been detected.

The reference concerns in particular the preliminary results presented in 1915 by the American astronomer Vesto Slipher.[15] De Sitter thus indicates the three radial velocities measured in his time by more than one observer, that of the Andromeda Nebula (-311 km/s), of NGC 1068 (+925 km/s), and of NGC 4594 (+1185 km/s). He takes the average (+600 km/s) and deduces that the radius of his space model is given by $R = 3 \times 10^{11}$ astronomical units.[16] But above all, he adds, "If, however, continued observation should confirm the fact that the spiral nebulae have systematically positive radial velocities, this would certainly be an indication to adopt the hypothesis B [his] in preference to A [Einstein's]."[17]

De Sitter was thus "on the track" of the cosmological interpretation of redshifts. He did not go beyond, however, and if he described the resulting radial velocities as "distorted," it is because he kept in mind the conception of a static universe, whose intrinsic properties should not change over time.

Also, for the time being these were still only "mathematical curiosities." De Sitter's metrics could not seriously be considered as a plausible model of the universe, since the properties of space-time were understood to be independent of matter. This, at least, was the opinion of Einstein, for whom the Mach principle, as we have seen, required that the coefficients of the metric be determined by the distribution of matter.[18]

The true resolution of the dilemma was found in 1922 by the Russian mathematician and physicist Alexander Friedmann.

4. ALEXANDER FRIEDMANN (1888–1925)

Crack-brained research leads to unforeseen discoveries.
—PAUL VALÉRY, "ON POE'S EUREKA" (1921)[1]

ALEXANDER ALEXANDROVICH FRIEDMANN WAS BORN IN St. Petersburg (Russia) on June 29, 1888, into a musical family.[2] His father, Alexander Friedmann, was a composer and a dancer in the ballet of the Mariinsky Theater. His mother, Ludmila Vojacka, was a pianist and the daughter of Czech composer Hynek Vojacek.

In 1906, after graduating with the gold medal from the Second Saint Petersburg Gymnasium, a venerable secondary school, Friedmann enrolled at St. Petersburg University in the department of physics and mathematics, where he graduated in 1910 and was kept on in preparation for a teaching position.

In 1913 Friedmann began work at the atmospheric observatory in Pavlovsk, near St. Petersburg. There he was involved in studies in dynamic meteorology, observation of the atmosphere, and Earth's magnetism. At the beginning of 1914 Friedmann published an important paper, "On the Relationship of Air Temperature to Altitude," in which he considered the theoretical possibility that there existed an upper temperature inversion point in the stratosphere. That fall and until 1916, he volunteered for service in World War I in an aviation detachment, flying missions aboard Russian military aircraft as an expert in ballistics and bombing techniques.

Figure 4.1.
Russian physicist and mathematician Alexander Friedmann, August 1, 1916. Friedmann was a decorated military aviator and aviation instructor before making a name for himself in cosmology as "the man who proved Einstein wrong."[3] He is rightly regarded as one of the fathers of the Big Bang.

Between 1918 and 1920 he was a professor at Perm State University, and between 1920 and 1924 a professor at Petrograd State University (Petrograd was the new name given to St. Petersburg). There he taught physics and mathematics. It was during this period that he discovered the theory of general relativity.

Cut off from the international scientific literature during the war years and the Russian Revolution, Soviet scholars only became acquainted with the theory of general relativity several years later. In 1919, the experimental confirmation of the value of the deflection of light rays in the solar gravitational field, predicted by Einstein's theory, had a great impact. As soon as Friedmann was appointed to the university, he began to study general relativity with exceptional diligence. Undoubtedly the theory seduced him by the breadth of its implications, its clear and simple theoretical basis, and its elegant mathematical apparatus. He began to search for exact solutions, quickly realizing that with this new interpretation of gravitation, in which the nature of space and time is related to the distribution and movement of gravitating masses, the structure of the universe became for the first time the object of an exact scientific analysis.

A regular seminar was organized at the university's Institute of Physics. Friedmann and his colleague Vsevolod Konstantinovich Frederiks gave lessons on general relativity. According to physicist Vladimir Fock, who participated in the seminar, the styles of their presentations were very different. Frederiks emphasized the physical aspect of the theory and, not liking mathematical formulations, tried to make his presentations qualitative. Friedmann, on the other hand, placed his emphasis on mathematics and not physics, striving for rigor and completeness in the formulation and discussion of problems. Yuri Alexandrovitch Krutkoff, who would play an important role in disseminating Friedmann's work (see Chapter 5), also took part in the seminar and gave lectures.

In 1922, Frederiks published the first synthetic work in Russian on the foundations of general relativity.[4] It was based on his lecture notes from Petrograd and Moscow.

At the same time, Friedmann and Frederiks began to write a fundamental monograph on the theory of relativity. They set out to present the theory in all its logical rigor, assuming that the level of knowledge of their readers in mathematics and theoretical physics did not exceed that of faculty at Russian universities. Technical constraints led them to divide their project into five separate volumes.

The first would be devoted to the foundations of tensor calculus; the second, to the foundations of multidimensional geometry; the third, to electrodynamics; the fourth and a fifth, to the foundations of special and general relativity. Only the first volume was published, in 1924 in Leningrad.[5] (St. Petersburg's name was changed to Petrograd in 1914, then to Leningrad in 1924.)

Friedmann published his major opus on the curvature of space in the German journal *Zeitschrift für Physik*. At the same time, Friedmann also completed his own popular-level work, *Mir kak prostranstvo i vremya* (*The Universe as Space and Time*), which appeared in 1923. His second major cosmological article appeared in 1924. In 1925, he was appointed director of the Leningrad Geophysical Institute. In the summer of 1925, in the company of the aviator P. F. Fedosenko, he beat the altitude record in a stratospheric balloon, rising to 7,400 meters.

Friedmann died suddenly in Leningrad on September 16, 1925, from typhoid fever, at the age of thirty-seven.[6] In 1931, he was posthumously awarded the Lenin Prize for his outstanding scientific work.

Friedmann is buried in his hometown. An instructive anecdote is worth telling. The location of the Russian scientist's grave was quickly forgotten, especially since the Stalinist regime that followed was hardly inclined to perpetuate the memory of this renowned "creationist" scientist. In 1988, the Alexander Friedmann Laboratory of the University of St. Petersburg (then called Leningrad State University) decided to organize the first "A. Friedmann International Seminar in Cosmology" to honor the centenary of the scientist's birth. The director of the Friedmann Institute, my friend Andrey Grib, had the idea of a search for Friedmann's tomb, planning a small commemorative ceremony in which admirers from various countries would participate. A venerable professor at the Institute of Physics and Technology in St. Petersburg and a former PhD student of Friedmann, Georgy Grinberg, remembered having attended the funeral of the scientist at the Smolenskoye Cemetery, and that the cosmologist's grave was close to that of the great mathematician Leonhard Euler.

Grib therefore asked one of his students, Mihail Rosenberg, to go to the cemetery to locate the tomb—even hinting that this task would be recognized as part of his thesis work. When Mihail Rosenberg went to the cemetery and asked to consult the register of all the people buried here, the authorities replied that they had no information from prior to World War II. Rosenberg then asked to see the tomb of Leonhard Euler. After the war, he was told, Euler's remains were transferred to another cemetery. There remained at least the old location, which the authorities indicated to him. Rosenberg explored the surroundings but found no evidence of Friedmann's presence. He then began to quarrel with the authorities: How can the records have disappeared? At this point, an attendant approached and inquired about the dispute. The director of the cemetery replied that the student was looking for a certain "Friedmann." "Which Friedmann," asked the employee, "the one who discovered the non-static cosmological solution to Einstein's equations?"

"Yes, yes," exclaimed the student.

"Well, come with me, I'll show you!"

This is how the cosmologist's grave was discovered. The cemetery employee was none other than a former physicist who'd had to leave his research institute for lack of funds.

5. ON THE CURVATURE
OF SPACE (1922)

*The solution of curved space soothes our fear of infinity
and our reluctance to conceive of nothingness.*
J. THIBAUD[1]

FRIEDMANN TOOK THE STEP THAT EINSTEIN HAD NOT BEEN
ready to take: if one abandons the hypothesis of a static universe,
the relativistic cosmological problem comprises an infinite number of
solutions in which the metric varies as a function of time. He wrote:

> In their well-known works on general cosmological questions,
> Einstein and de Sitter arrive at two possible types of the universe:
> Einstein obtains the so-called cylindrical world, in which space
> possesses a constant curvature independent of time and in which
> the radius of curvature is connected with the total mass of matter
> existing in space. De Sitter obtains a spherical world in which not
> only space but also the world can be spoken of, in a certain sense,
> as a world of constant curvature. In doing so certain assumptions
> about the matter tensor are made by both Einstein and de Sit-
> ter; these correspond to the incoherence of matter and its being
> relatively at rest, e.g. the velocity of matter is assumed to be suf-
> ficiently small in comparison with the fundamental velocity, the
> velocity of light.
>   The goal of this notice is, first, the derivation of the cylindrical
> and spherical worlds (as special cases) from some general assump-
> tions and, second, the proof of the possibility of a world whose

spatial curvature is constant with respect to three coordinates that are permissible spatial coordinates and that depend on the time, e.g. on the fourth (time) coordinate. This new type is, as far as its remaining properties are concerned, an analogue of the Einsteinian cylindrical universe.[2]

Thus begins this founding "notice" of non-static cosmology. Received on June 29, 1922, by the German journal *Zeitschrift für Physik*, it was published shortly afterwards. Friedmann demonstrates "the possibility of a world whose space curvature is constant with respect to three coordinates that are permissible spatial coordinates and that depend on the time, e.g. on the fourth (time) coordinate," and he indicates the metric, which will later be called Friedmann's metric.

Friedmann discusses the case of a homogeneous and isotropic universe, i.e., with a constant density of matter in space. The relationship between matter distribution and curvature, stipulated by Einstein's equations, requires that the spatial curvature of the universe be uniform (constant at each point in space at a given instant).

In this first article, Friedmann considers only the case of a positive spatial curvature. If the radius of curvature R is independent of time, he demonstrates, the only solutions are the static universes of Einstein and de Sitter. If $R(t)$ depends on the time variable, there are an infinite number of non-static models, in monotonic expansion or in periodic oscillation, depending on the value chosen for the cosmological constant λ. The latter, introduced by Einstein and adopted by de Sitter to ensure the existence of static solutions, is no longer necessary; as Friedmann writes, it is "an extra constant in the problem." It can nevertheless be retained, and its various possible values generate a variety of models. If it is positive and above a certain critical value, the radius of curvature of the universe grows monotonically from an initial zero value; the model is said to be *monotonic of the first kind*. If λ is positive but below the critical value, the radius of curvature of the universe grows monotonically from a non-zero initial value; the model is said to be *monotonic of second kind*. Finally, if $\lambda \leq 0$, we obtain a *periodic universe* with alternating eras of expansion and contraction, where the curvature radius varies between 0 and a finite value. Its period increases with λ, but Friedmann notes that if $\lambda = 0$, the period depends only on the total mass of the universe.

Friedmann does not give a graphical representation of the $R(t)$ curves obtained in the various cases. For a better understanding of his results, Figure 5.1 summarizes the three types of time evolution predicted by the Russian cosmologist.

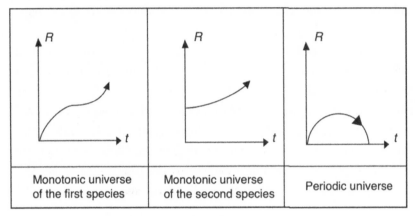

Figure 5.1.

Friedmann's three possible patterns of cosmic evolution.

- Monotonic universe of the first species: R varies from 0 to ∞
- Monotonic universe of the second species: R varies from R_0 to ∞
- Periodic Universe: R varies between 0 and a maximum

In the case of the periodic universe, the question arises as to whether the universe experiences a single "arc," beginning in one singularity (later called the "Big Bang") and ending in another singularity (the "Big Crunch"), or whether it is in perpetual oscillation, with cycles of expansion and contraction continuing eternally. Friedmann thus clarifies his thought:

> With respect to the periodic world, two viewpoints are possible: if we regard two events to be coincident if their space coordinates coincide and the difference of the time coordinates is an integer multiple of the period, then the curvature radius increases from 0 to x_0 and then decreases to the value 0; the time of the world's

existence is finite; on the other hand, if the time varies between - ∞ and + ∞ (i.e., we consider two events to be coincident only when not only their space coordinates but also their world coordinates coincide), then we arrive at a true periodicity of the space curvature.

Lemaître dubbed Friedmann's periodic model the "phoenix universe."[3] That model was abandoned for various reasons. (See Chapter 13.)

It only remained for Friedmann to link his models to astronomical observations and to try to quantify his predictions about the age of the universe. To do so, he relied on the theoretical calculation of the expansion-contraction period of the cyclic solution, related to the total mass of the universe and the cosmological constant. By taking into account some observational data relating to the average star density and the size of the observable universe, Friedmann could estimate the mass of the universe. He concluded his paper with this remarkable prediction:

> Our knowledge is completely insufficient to carry out numerical calculations and to decide which world our universe is; it is possible that the causality problem and the problem of the centrifugal force will illuminate these questions. It is left to remark that the "cosmological" quantity λ remains undetermined in our formulae, since it is an extra constant in the problem; possibly electrodynamical considerations can lead to its evaluation. If we set $\lambda = 0$ and $M = 5.10^{21}$ solar masses, then the world period becomes of the order of 10 billion years. But these figures can surely only serve as an illustration for our calculations.

The value of ten billion years was much greater than the age of the oldest objects in the universe as estimated at the time. In the early 1920s, the age of the Earth, inferred from the period of radium decay, was considered to be no more than one billion years, before being later revised upwards by a large margin. As we will see, the figures put forward today for the age of the universe confirm that Friedmann's prediction was relatively close.

Friedmann's article was ahead of its time, as one can also see from the fact that anybody studying modern cosmology can immediately recognize its main equations. While the formulations of the various metrics (de Sitter's as well as Friedmann's) would later change to the unified form of Howard Robertson and Arthur Walker, the differential equations that govern the time development of a space of constant positive curvature have not changed one iota.

Einstein's Reaction

With his 1922 article, Friedmann introduced a scientific revolution of the same magnitude as the Copernican revolution. In pre-Copernican cosmology, space was centered on a very particular place, the Earth. In pre-Friedmannian cosmology, the universe was static, in the sense of not evolving. Friedmannian cosmology introduces the historicity of the universe as space-time, as well as the idea of a beginning.

But the scientific community of the 1920s was not prepared to receive these "curious facts," (more on this in Chapter 6) as Friedmann called them in his popular book. Leading the skeptics was Einstein. *Zeitschrift für Physik* was the most widely read physics journal of the time. The father of relativity noticed Friedmann's article and reacted quickly in that venue. On September 18, 1922, he published a short "remark" in the journal, in which he claimed that Friedmann had made a calculation error and that solutions with variable radius were incompatible with relativity.

"In the cited work, the results concerning a nonstationary world appear to me suspicious. In reality it turns out the solution does not satisfy the field equations," he wrote.[4] In fact, it was Einstein himself who committed a miscalculation.[5] But a series of fortuitous circumstances would delay the recognition of this error for several months.

The issue of the journal *Zeitschrift für Physik* containing Einstein's objection reached Russia in October 1922. Friedmann and his colleagues—in particular Frederiks—read it, and Friedmann decided to reply by postal mail. He did not send his letter to the journal's editorial office but to Einstein himself, thus showing a certain deference toward his prestigious opponent. In fact, it is likely that Friedmann had read Einstein's criticism a little earlier, as can be seen from the beginning of his letter:

Dear Professor,

From the letter of a friend of mine who is now abroad, I had the honor to learn that you have submitted a short note to be printed in the volume 11 of the *Zeitschrift für Physik*, where it is stated that if one accepts the assumptions made in my article "On the Curvature of Space," it will follow from the world equations you derived, that the radius of curvature of the world is a quantity independent of time.[6]

The friend in question mostly likely was Yuri Alexandrovitch Krutkoff, who would play for a few months the role of "messenger" between Einstein and Friedmann.[7]

The Messenger

Krutkoff was one of the most cultivated Russian physicists of his time. He studied special relativity with Paul Ehrenfest between 1907 and 1912, and in 1920 he participated in the seminar at Petrograd University organized by Friedmann and Frederiks on general relativity. In the many notebooks and correspondence Krutkoff left behind, we learn that in 1922–1923 he spent "a year and a day" in Germany. More precisely, Krutkoff arrived in Berlin at the end of September 1922, shortly after the publication of Einstein's remark. Thus, he probably read Einstein's criticism and informed Friedmann before the journal itself reached Friedmann in St. Petersburg. (No correspondence between Krutkoff and Friedmann has been found, but further developments, as we will see, suggest Krutkoff's hand in this matter.)

In his letter to Einstein, Friedmann showed by direct calculations that the cancelation of the divergence of the stress-energy tensor made it impossible to obtain a constant radius of curvature in time.[8] Friedmann wrote, "Considering that the possible existence of a nonstationary world is of some interest, will allow myself to present you here the calculations I have made for verification and critical assessment."

Friedmann then specified that he had recently studied "the case of a world with constant negative curvature and variable time... The possibility of obtaining from your world equations a solution with constant negative curvature is of exceptional interest to me, and I therefore ask you, although I know you are very busy, to reply to my letter."

This passage proves that Friedmann had already discovered the negative curvature solutions in 1922, but they were not published until two years later. Friedmann concludes his letter thus: "Should you find the calculations presented in my letter correct, please be so kind as to inform the editors of *Zeitschrift für Physik* about it; perhaps in this case you will publish a correction to your statement or provide an opportunity for this letter to be printed."

Friedmann was right to assume that Einstein was "very busy." Weeks went by without getting an answer. The explanation is simple: by the time the letter reached Berlin in December, Einstein had left the city. At the end of September, two weeks after sending his commentary on Friedmann's article, he and his wife embarked on a long journey that took them first through Switzerland and France. On October 11, they embarked for Japan. During this trip, Einstein learned that he had been awarded the Nobel Prize in Physics. He could not reach Stockholm in time for the award ceremony.[9]

It wasn't until March 1923, after passing through Palestine, France, and Spain, that Einstein returned to Berlin. Of course, it took him some time to sort through the mail that had accumulated during his absence of almost six months.

In May, Einstein was invited to Holland, to the University of Leiden—where he was an honorary professor—to attend Hendrick Lorentz's last public lecture. Krutkoff was in Leiden at the same time. Einstein met him at the home of his friend Ehrenfest, where he always stayed when he was in Holland. (Einstein had already heard favorably of Krutkoff, as correspondence between Max Born and Einstein testifies.[10])

Krutkoff's conversations with the great physicist can be traced from his diary notes and the letters he sent to his sister, Tatiana Krutkova. The diary for May 1923 is covered with formulas from Friedmann's article and related calculations. In one of the letters, Krutkoff writes, "On Monday, May 7, 1923, I was reading together with Einstein Friedmann's article in *Zeitschrift für Physik*." In another letter of May 18, Krutkoff says, "At five o'clock, Einstein reported to Ehrenfest, Droite, and a Belgian on his latest paper... I defeated Einstein in the argument against Friedmann. Petrograd's honor was saved!"[11]

It is not known whether at the time of this interview Einstein had already read Friedmann's letter to him, or whether it was the interview with Krutkoff that persuaded him to sort his mail on his return to Berlin. In any case, on May 16, 1923, Einstein returned to Berlin, and on May 21 he submitted his second note on Friedmann's article to the *Zeitschrift für Physik*. The text, very brief, is as follows:

> In an earlier note I exercised criticism on the mentioned paper. My objection, however, was based on a calculation error—as I have become persuaded, at the suggestion of Mr. Krutkoff, guided by a letter by Mr. Friedmann. I consider Mr. Friedmann's results correct and illuminating. It is demonstrated that the field equations permit, aside from the static solution, dynamic (i.e., variable with the time coordinate), centrally symmetrical solutions for the structure of space.[12]

Does this mean that Einstein finally accepted Friedmann's discovery as being of such a nature as to draw a new image of the universe? This is unlikely, as his later reticence towards Lemaître's work will also show. An investigation by John Stachel has found a first (unpublished) version of the note, in which, to the last sentence of the manuscript—"the field equations permit... dynamic solutions"—Einstein added, "to which it is hardly possible to attribute physical meaning."[13] This sentence, however, he deleted at the last moment. It is similar to the sentence he would later write, in 1927, against the work of Lemaître. (See Chapter 9.) Einstein's attitude towards the cosmological problem thus reflected an uneasiness that would never really be resolved.

Missed Chances

In August and September 1923, Friedmann stayed in Berlin and tried to meet Einstein. On August 9, Krutkoff wrote to his sister:

"Friedmann is here; today, in a few hours, he leaves for Hamburg. Einstein's note, in which he is rehabilitated thanks to my intervention, has already come out."[14]

On August 19, Friedmann writes to N. Malinina (his future wife): "My trip is going badly—Einstein, for example, has left Berlin for vacation, and I won't be able to see him."

September 2: "The only things I have to do are: 1) visit Göttingen; 2) see Pahlen (an astronomer who was my collaborator); 3) see Mises (the publisher of *Zeitschrift für Ang. Math.*) and Einstein."

September 13: "Today I visited the astronomer Pahlen, an old friend of mine.[15] There I met the astronomer Freundlich, a very interesting person, we talked about the structure of the universe."

Friedmann, Pahlen, and Freundlich remain somewhat associated in the history of astronomy by the fact that three craters on the Moon bear their names. Friedmann had known Pahlen in St. Petersburg before World War I, and during the war they met in Kiev as part of the same aviation team. The other astronomer mentioned in the letter, Erwin Finlay Freundlich (1885–1964), worked in 1911 with Einstein on the orbit of Mercury. In 1916 he published in Berlin a popular science book, *The Foundations of Einstein's Theory of Gravitation*, of which Einstein had written the preface. In 1918, he resigned from his position in Berlin to work full-time with Einstein.[16] He was later the founder and first director of the Einstein Institute in Potsdam.

Friedmann did not manage to meet Einstein in 1923, nor in April of the following year during his second visit to Germany, when he attended the International Technical Mechanics Congress in Delft, Holland. However, his letter of September 13, 1923, cheerfully notes, "Everyone was very impressed with my struggle with Einstein and my final victory; I am pleased, because as far as my articles are concerned, I could now publish them more easily."

6. THE WORLD
AS SPACE AND TIME (1923)

Thou hast arranged all things by measure and number and weight.
BOOK OF WISDOM

IN PARALLEL WITH HIS ADVANCED RESEARCH, FRIEDMANN ALSO completed his popularizing work *Mir kak prostranstvo i vremya* (*The World as Space and Time*),[1] which Friedmann dated September 5, 1922. It followed closely his fundamental article "On the Curvature of Space," completed on May 19, so that in the last part Friedmann could incorporate the major cosmological results he had just obtained.

The 131-page book came out in Petrograd in 1923, in the "Contemporary Culture" series offered by the publisher Academia. The print run of three thousand copies was normal for the time. A second edition was published forty-two years later in Moscow, by Nauka, with a print run of 45,000 copies. A third edition was published in 1966, as part of the collection of *Selected Works of A. A. Friedmann*.

The book has an introduction and three chapters respectively entitled Space, Time, and Gravitation. It is essentially an axiomatic exposition of the theory of general relativity, with Friedmann addressing the cosmological question only as a particular field of application of the theory, in the last paragraphs of the last chapter. The first chapter is devoted to the study of the general properties of space (metrics, geodesics, curvature, etc.). The second chapter is devoted to the union of space and time as envisaged by relativity.

Friedmann deals directly with general relativity without going through the "pedagogical" stage of special relativity. Since general relativity was elaborated after special relativity, between 1911 and 1916, over the course of time both specialized and popularized presentations of general relativity followed that of special relativity. Einstein himself had set the example. Friedmann thus deviates from the (still new) tradition by favoring the logical approach over the historical one. According to him, the theory of general relativity is not only an extension of the special theory—the latter being valid in weak gravitational fields; it is simply more *fundamental* and, for this reason, must be presented first.

The third chapter describes the methods used by Einstein's general relativity, and by Hermann Weyl's alternative theory, to build a representation of the universe.

In the book's introduction, Friedmann defends himself against any possible criticism for having written a work of scientific popularization:

> The discussed topic makes me think that, gaining some *real* knowledge of the principle of relativity on the pages of a philosophical journal could be helpful and useful. Speaking of real knowledge I am against some attempts and explanations, which try to provide a superficial popularization of the relativity principle, which could not be popularized without extreme care. Such popularizations are usually achieved at the price of abuses of its ideas and scientific meaning. From this, it is clear, I hope, that this work does not in any case pretend to be popular and requires some knowledge in advanced mathematics in order to be understood.[2]

He obviously did not appreciate the popular science genre, although he had several such works in his personal library. According to him, relativity was a fashionable subject, but "impossible to popularize." But could the subject be made at least somewhat more accessible? It was certainly a timely moment to try. In a country barely emerging from gigantic upheavals, where life was resuming its normal course after many years of war and famine, public interest in the theory of relativity was surging. As the French writer Emmanuel Berl wrote in his novel *Sylvia*, "The war had left a certain despair in the heart of everyone; the post-war period was, nevertheless, a time of hope, of secret faith... There was, after all, no shortage of tonics: the revolutionaries had Lenin, the industrialists had Ford, the scientists Einstein, the psychologists Freud."[3]

Another cultural factor also came into play. Cosmology deals with eternal questions about the nature of the world and offers a field for reflection on humanity's place in the universe. It is therefore not without reason that public lectures on relativity attracted a large audience, and that books and articles on the subject quickly sold out despite their large print runs.

By 1923 about twenty books on relativity had already been published in Russian. Half of them were translations of foreign—mostly German—books. One by Einstein himself, *Relativity: The Special and the General Theory; A Popular Exposition*, had several editions in Russian, including two published in Petrograd in 1921 and 1922. The 1916 German edition was in Friedmann's personal library. There was also Erwin Finlay Freundlich's book, *Foundations of Einstein's Gravitation Theory*, with a preface by Einstein, whose Russian translation had been edited by Frederiks; along with I. Lehmann's *Theory of Relativity*, E. Cassirer's *Theory of Relativity*, and Max Born's *Theory of Relativity*. The monographs of Charles Nordmann and Henri Bergson were also available in Russian translation.

Yet, despite its author's denial, *The World as Space and Time* is indeed a text of scientific popularization, though written not for the general public but for philosophers. This at least was Friedmann's ambition, since his text was originally intended for the philosophy journal *Mysl (Thought)*. Indeed, he believed that "the height of vision and the boldness of ideas characterizing the general concepts of relativity over space and time must undoubtedly somewhat mark, if not influence, the development of ideas among modern philosophers."[4]

It is not known why the text was not published in this journal, though certainly a 131-page article is not suitable for a journal. It is also possible that the content and level were not appropriate. In any case, it must be acknowledged that his project of "popularization for philosophers" was not a perfect success. Friedmann's own literary style is awkward, suffering from a great deal of repetition, heaviness, and stiffness of language. As for the content and the level of technicality, Friedmann was somewhat naïve to believe that philosophers would be able to penetrate the mysteries of relativity by reading his book.

What is interesting about the work lies elsewhere—specifically, in four areas:

- Its axiomatic exposition of the problems of space, time, and gravitation

- Its discussion of the attempt at geometric unification of gravitation and electromagnetism, due to Weyl

- Its assertion that the "creation of the universe" appears naturally as the solution to the equations of the gravitational field

- Its remarks on the topological indetermination of general relativity

Let's look at these points one by one.

The Axiomatization of Relativity

Friedmann leads the reader to the very heart of the subject (the nature of space and time) through axiomatics, not physics. This particular approach is that of David Hilbert (1862–1943).[5]

A recognition of the need for an axiomatization, first of mathematics and then of physics, originated in the middle of the nineteenth century. It occurred when the construction of hyperbolic non-euclidean geometry by Carl Friedrich Gauss, Nicolai Lobachevski, and Janos Bolyai forced an abandonment of claims of absolute truth for euclidean geometry. From then on, mathematical axioms no longer appear as obvious, but as hypotheses that must be verified as being adapted to the representation of the sensible world.

Gauss was, for example, convinced that the debate among the various geometries could be resolved by experience. As Friedmann recalls in his book, Gauss even tried to prove this by testing the geometry of space by means of geodetic measurements.

Friedmann also repeatedly quotes Friedrich Bernhard Riemann's famous habilitation dissertation, *On the Hypotheses Which Lie at the Foundation of Geometry* (1867). Riemann's ambition was precisely to provide a general mathematical framework for various natural phenomena: since there can no longer be unlimited trust in the failing classical geometric intuition, geometry must be axiomatized without resorting to intuition.

The most famous achievements in the axiomatization of euclidean geometry were in Hilbert's 1899 *Grundlagen der Geometrie*.[6] This work almost immediately became the "charter" of modern axiomatics. In addition to providing a complete system of valid axioms for euclidean geometry, Hilbert classified these axioms into various groups of a different nature and attempted to determine the exact scope of each of these groups of axioms. For example, the non-euclidean geometries of Nikolai Lobachevski and Riemann appear as simple special cases obtained by suppressing or modifying this or that axiom. Hilbert thus clearly emphasized the freedom of the mathematician in the choice of his hypotheses. This view was quickly adopted, almost unanimously, by mathematicians; it would develop throughout the first half of the twentieth century, momentarily crowned by the work of Nicolas Bourbaki,[7] then definitively limited by that of Kurt Gödel.[8]

Hilbert took his reflection further by claiming to axiomatize the whole of physics. In 1915, Hilbert published *Grundlagen der Physik* (where he provided the equations of general relativity, as mentioned above). It was indeed the time when physics was definitively rooted in mathematics, and the critical analysis of the logical foundations of the latter necessarily had to refer to the former. It was in this climate that Friedmann wrote his book on relativity.

From the very first paragraphs, Friedmann insists on the problem of *physical interpretation*. Mathematicians are indeed embarrassed by new concepts until they can give a physical, sensible interpretation. This had been the case with negative numbers and imaginary numbers. But by the nineteenth century, mathematicians had begun to feel clearly that it was legitimate to reason about objects that had no such physical interpretation. For example, in his dissertation, Riemann had been careful not to speak of points, but of "determinations," since metric relations could "be studied only for abstract quantities and represented only by formulas."[9] Because of the sheer number of possible interpretations or models, it came to be understood that the nature of mathematical objects was basically secondary. The essence of mathematics now appeared to be the study of relations between objects that are no longer known, that are described by only a few of their properties, precisely those that we put at the base as axioms of theory. This is the thesis to which Friedmann fully adheres.

The Russian physicist also uses the term "arithmetization," which may surprise the reader. What does arithmetic have to do with relativity? Here again, the context of the time must be remembered. Arithmetic deals with natural integers, "exclusive products of our mind," as Gauss wrote in 1832, opposing them to the notion of space.[10] Karl Weierstrass, however, obtained a model of positive rational numbers or negative integers by considering classes of pairs of natural integers. Then Georg Cantor and Richard Dedekind managed to find an arithmetic model of irrational numbers. From that moment on, integers became the foundation of all classical mathematics. Real numbers were interpreted in terms of integers; complex numbers and euclidean geometry were as well (thanks to analytical geometry). Finally, Eugenio Beltrami and Felix Klein obtained euclidean models of the non-euclidean geometries of Lobachevski and Riemann, and subsequently arithmetized these theories.

Models based on arithmetic became all the more important as the axiomatic method developed, and with it the conception of mathematical objects as free creations of the mind. Demonstrating the existence of a mathematical object with given properties is simply constructing an object with the given properties. This is what arithmetic models are for. We then speak of the class of objects having such-and-such a property. In his "logical calculation" of 1847, the Englishman George Boole[11] did not hesitate to introduce the Universe as a set of all objects!

This is how Friedmann defines space and time: in terms of a class of objects arithmetized by means of such-and-such a property. He sees arithmetization as a universal procedure to describe numerically any property of any object.

Let us note in passing that Friedmann gives the following example of arithmetization: Human beings have the property of being gendered. Let's match the property of being female with the number 0, the property of being male with the number 1; this rule defines the arithmetization of the class of sexes. P. Y. Polubarinova-Kochina, a student of Friedmann's who became a Member of the Soviet Academy of Sciences, reported that, not appreciating this example, "the women working in Friedmann's department expressed their indignation to Alexander Alexandrovich... He promised them to choose another example for the second edition."[12] But the second edition did not see the light of day during Friedmann's lifetime.

In any case, it is clear that the axiomatization of space and time has little pedagogical value; one of the originalities—on the physical and not the mathematical level—of Friedmann's presentation of the subject is therefore also one of its limitations.

The Geometric Unification of Gravitation and Electromagnetism

The theory of special relativity—originally conceived as a physical theory of electrodynamics—was geometrized by Henri Poincaré, then by Hermann Minkowski (1864–1909). The name of the latter remains attached to the formalism of four-dimensional space-time, the mathematical basis of all future relativistic developments.[13] Historically, general relativity was constructed as a geometrical theory of gravitation.[14] The latter is no longer described in terms of force, but in terms of the metric of a Riemannian space.

German physicist Hermann Weyl was the first to attempt to extend Riemannian geometry to incorporate electromagnetism and gravitation into a unified formalism.[15] He used non-metric connections; but in its original form, his attempt later proved to be a failure. Nevertheless, the theory was beautiful. In its mathematical aspect, it played an essential role in the development of modern differential geometry and in the elaboration of gauge theories. As for its physical aspect, it was an extension of the wish expressed by Hilbert in his 1915 article and would haunt without result the mind of physicists throughout the twentieth century: to treat *all* forces of Nature (and not only gravitation) as manifestations of the structure of space-time.[16]

The fundamental importance of these questions is reflected in the place Friedmann gives to Weyl's approach. While acknowledging that theory is by no means proven by experience, the Russian physicist shows a certain preference for Weyl's approach over Einstein's more modest one.

It is interesting to note what was to be the fate after 1922 of the attempts to geometrize electromagnetism. Two approaches can be distinguished: either the generalization of the geometry of space-time to four dimensions—a path taken by Weyl, Eddington, Cartan, and Einstein; or the addition of an extra dimension to space-time—a path adopted by Kaluza-Klein's theory.

Regarding the first way, the French mathematician Elie Cartan proposed in 1922 an extension of the Riemannian geometry using connections that were not necessarily symmetrical on its two lower indices. He suspected that the tensor obtained in this way, today called Cartan's torsion, could be related to electrodynamics. In this context, the letters on absolute parallelism exchanged between Cartan and Einstein in the period 1922–1929 are very interesting (the name "absolute parallelism" comes from the fact that in this theory, the Riemann curvature tensor, distinct from the Riemann-Christoffel tensor used in general relativity, is everywhere zero).[17] Following them, Einstein published a series of articles in the reports of the Prussian Academy of Sciences about absolute parallelism and a unified field theory. One of them summarizes the various papers proposing field equations that include the torsion tensor and lead, as a first approximation, to both Maxwell's equations and Newton-Poisson's equations. Unfortunately, Einstein never tried to incorporate quantum mechanics into his scheme. Other physicists preferred to explore the path of quantum field theory rather than follow him in his approach. Thus, Einstein's unitary theory project, lacking a description of particles, failed.

The second path was taken by the Austrian physicist Theodor Kaluza (1885–1945) and the Swedish physicist Oscar Klein (1894–1977). They independently developed a theory of five-dimensional space that today bears their names.[18] In their model, the description of electromagnetism requires the introduction of a "fifth" dimension. However, this dimension is not orthogonal to "our" four-dimensional space-time. The four directing cosines of the "angles" that this new dimension makes with our usual dimensions depend on the point in space-time, and form the four components of the vector potential of the electromagnetic field. From the point of view of this theory, charged particles move in a penta-dimensional space-time, whereas we human beings only perceive the projection of this movement in the four-dimensional space-time. This can be illustrated by the analogy of an airplane's shadow moving on the surface of the Earth.[19] The movement of the shadow depends not only on the trajectory of the plane, but also on the position of the sun in the sky. Therefore, even if the plane's trajectory is straight, the movement of its shadow is not. It is the same in Kaluza-Klein's theory; the projection of the motion varies according to the points in space-time, and the "shadow" of the charge does not move along a straight line. This geodesic deviation is interpreted as an effect of electrical and magnetic forces.

Kaluza-Klein's model, abandoned for electromagnetism, has been taken up and generalized in modern theories of particle physics, in particular in the *superstring theory*, where the number of additional dimensions reaches seven or even more.[20] These additional dimensions are different from the usual spatial dimensions in that they are compacted, i.e., they take the form of a circle in the plane, with a radius of curvature that can be as small as 10^{-33} centimeters.

The fact that no change of scale was observed when looping in space led Weyl himself to abandon his model. Later, however, E. Schrödinger, V. A. Fock, and other researchers working on quantum theory developed Weyl's idea and came to formulate the so-called *gauge* theory. According to the latter, it is not the scale of macroscopic bodies that can change from one point in space-time to another, but a certain characteristic of the quantum object: the phase of its wave function. This has the effect of transforming the usual derivatives, which are involved in the equations giving the wave functions of charged particles, into generalized derivatives depending on the electromagnetic field. Gauge theories have proved to be successful in describing not only electromagnetic interactions, but also weak and strong interactions of elementary particles. Weyl's theory for gravity alone is sometimes discussed in a form close to its original, in so-called *conformal gravity theories*. These theories are studied as possible starting models of quantum gravity, an unsolved problem.

Attempts to unify gravitation and electromagnetism by geometrization of the latter have given rise to numerous works, including those of Mie, Weyl, Eddington, Klein, Schrödinger, and Pauli. Eddington wanted to generalize Weyl's theory by starting from a variety with an affine connection (parallel transport), and by decomposing the curvature tensor into a symmetrical part (ordinary Ricci tensor of a metric space) and an antisymmetric part, the latter playing the role of the electromagnetic field.[21]

The Creation of the Universe

In 1924, Friedmann worked with the Dutch mathematician Jan Arnoldus Schouten on a geometric model of electromagnetism inspired by Weyl's model.[22] However, Friedmann's innovation was not in this direction, but in the one that follows.

At the end of his book *The World as Space and Time*, Friedmann presents, albeit very briefly, the dynamic solutions he had discovered and published in technical form in 1922 in *Zeitschrift für Physik*. Thus, it is the first popularized formulation in the history of cosmology of the concepts of an expanding or contracting universe and a cosmic singularity.

Here is the key passage summarizing the new relativistic cosmology:

It is possible to arrive at two types of universe: 1) *stationary type*—the curvature of space does not change with time, and 2) *non-stationary type*—the curvature of space changes with time. A sphere, whose radius does not change with time, can serve as an illustration of the first type (stationary) universe. The two-dimensional surface of the sphere is a two-dimensional space of constant curvature. Conversely, the second type of universe can be pictured as a sphere which changes all the time—either expanding or reducing its radius.... The stationary type of universe allows only two cases for the universe, which were studied by Einstein and de Sitter. Einstein determined, using the existing astronomical data,[23] that the radius of the curvature of the universe is 10^{12}–10^{13} distances from the Earth to the Sun, and that the density ρ (everywhere constant) is 10^{26} g/cm^3. In de Sitter's model of the universe there is complete absence of density of gravitating masses ($\rho = 0$).

The non-stationary type of universe presents a great variety of cases: for this type there may exist cases when the radius of the curvature of the world, starting from some magnitude, constantly increases with time; there may further exist cases when the radius of curvature changes periodically: the universe contracts into a point (into nothingness), then again, increases its radius from a point to a given magnitude,... again reduces the radius of its curvature, turns into a point and so on.[24]

Thus, it is obvious that Friedmann already knew about closed and open space-time when he wrote his book, and that he fully appreciated the implications of the discovery for the real universe.

Contrary to what has often been claimed, Friedmann's cosmo-logical work cannot be reduced to a simple mathematical problem. As far as the cosmic singularity (the universe reduced to a point) is concerned, Friedmann posed for the first time the problem of the beginning and the end of the universe in scientific terms.[25] He could not help but see a metaphysical implication; as he wrote, "This unwittingly brings to mind the saga of the Hindu mythology about the periods of life; there also appears a possibility to speak about 'the creation of the world from nothing,' but all of that should be viewed as curious facts which cannot be solidly confirmed by the insufficient astronomical material."[26]

The concepts of cyclic or oscillatory universes are indeed quite frequently encountered in mythology. According to Hinduism, each cycle of the universe is a *kalpa*, or day of Brahma, which lasts 4.32 billion years. Vishnu, who controls the universe, has a life of one hundred "cosmic years," each containing 360 days of Brahma. After 36,000 cycles, corresponding to about 150 trillion earth years, the world comes to an end, and only the Spirit survives. After an indeterminate period of time, a new world and a new Vishnu emerge, and the cycle begins again. Note that the day of Brahma is of roughly the same order as the age of the universe in modern cosmology—that is, measured in billions of years. For those attracted to Hindu thought, an oscillating universe model, or both, this coincidence is likely to be greeted with interest. (But again, see Chapter 13 for some of the problems facing the oscillating universe model.)

The alternate interpretation, the "creation of the world out of nothing," also finds precedent in ancient religious texts—explicitly in the Second Book of Maccabees 7:28 and arguably as well in Genesis 1 and John 1.

Once launched in the field of relativistic cosmology, the idea of a cosmic singularity has caused many upheavals and misunderstandings, and it posed a psychological block for many physicists of the time.

The idea of a cosmic singularity, which Friedmann described as a "curiosity"—perhaps out of modesty, or perhaps to distance himself once again from hazardous theological interpretations—has become a major challenge to contemporary research, as it is closely linked to the unsolved problem of quantum gravity.[27]

In Friedmann's general bibliography, we note the existence of a lost manuscript, entitled *Creation* (*Mirozdanie*). No one knows what its contents might have been, but it is not impossible that Friedmann developed a theological point of view in it—a point of view that he refuses to address in his popularizing book, as he points out on several occasions. Under the Communist regime, talking about the creation of the universe was politically daring.[28] It was only in the 1960s that Soviet science became converted to the Big Bang concept.[29]

Here one must say some words about Friedmann's religious beliefs. He was an Orthodox Christian, if not necessarily a fully orthodox one. The only discipline at the St. Peterburg gymnasium in which the young pupil Alexander Friedmann had mainly excellent marks (5/5) was catechism. At the same time his marks in mathematics were only 3 (i.e., "satisfactory"). Friedmann married his first wife, E. N. Dorofeeva, in the church. V. V. Doynikova remembered conversations with Friedmann about his religious faith. It is interesting that some of them were of a mystical nature. Friedmann, we are told, "was fond of the 'occult' in general [and] thought that he could cure a toothache by [his] words" alone. Friedmann had people close to him who were deeply religious, including Vladimir Ivanovich Smirnov, the famous Russian mathematician.[30]

On Friedmann's grave in the Smolenskoie graveyard in St. Petersburg there is the Orthodox cross. Maybe this was done according to his last will, or made by his relatives who knew about his attitude to faith. In 1925, just before his death, when he was Director of the Main Geophysical Observatory at a time of antireligious and antichurch persecutions by the Communist regime, he married, according to Orthodox Christian rule, his second wife, N. E. Malinina, in the church of Simferopol, in Crimea.

So the "creation of the world" was not a matter of empty words for him. One might say that in his work Friedmann realized Dostoevsky's idea in *The Brothers Karamazov* that it might take a non-euclidean mind to solve the contradiction between science and religious revelation. V. V. Doynikova remembered that Dostoevsky was one of Friedmann's favorite writers.

Now let us return to Friedmann's discussion of the age of the universe. "In the absence of reliable astronomical data," he commented, "it is useless to give any numbers characterizing the 'life' of the non-stationary universe; if nevertheless, for the sake of curiosity, we try to calculate the time elapsed from the moment when the universe was created starting from a point to its present state, that is, when we try to determine therefore the time that elapsed from the creation of the world, then we obtain a number in the tens of billions of our ordinary years."[31]

Friedmann relied here on the theoretical calculation of the expansion-contraction period of his cyclic solution, which he carried out in his article in *Zeitschrift für Physik*. We have seen that by adopting the value of 5×10^{21} solar masses for the mass of the universe and neglecting the cosmological constant, he deduced an age on the order of ten billion years.

At the time Friedmann wrote his book, he had no experimental information on the subject. He therefore exercised a brilliant intuition: the values he indicates for the age of the universe are close to what we deduce today from observations: 13.8 billion years, according to analyses of the data collected by the Planck satellite.

The Topological Question

It is also in the last chapter that Friedmann mentions the insufficiency of Einstein's equations for defining the global topology of the universe. Consequently, he wrote, several different topologies can be considered as the *same* solution of the equations. These topological aspects would be developed in his second technical article, published in 1924 in *Zeitschrift für Physik*. I will come back to this in Chapter 17 after examining Lemaître's work, because the topological concerns of both men are one of the deepest signs of their originality.

The general conclusion of Friedmann's book is this:

> Einstein's theory is confirmed by experience; it accounts for phenomena that have long remained unexplained, and it leads to new and fascinating predictions. The most correct and profound method to explore the geometry of the world and the structure of the Cosmos according to Einstein's theory is to apply this theory to the universe as a whole and to use astronomical observations. At present this method does not give any convincing results, because the mathematical analysis is still weak, given the difficulties of the problem, and there are too few astronomical data to support a solid experimental study of the world. But these are only temporary obstacles; our descendants will undoubtedly discover the true nature of the Cosmos that hosts us.

7. SPACE WITH NEGATIVE CURVATURE (1924)

In science, the authority of a thousand is not worth
the humble reasoning of a single individual.
—GALILEO GALILEI (1632)

IN 1924, ALEXANDER FRIEDMANN'S SECOND FUNDAMENTAL
cosmological article, "On the Possibility of a World with Constant
Negative Curvature of Space," was published in *Zeitschrift für Physik.*[1]
The article is dated November 1923. Following an idea articulated
by V. Fock,[2] Friedmann considers the negative curvature models and
demonstrates the existence of non-static solutions with positive matter
density, all characterized by monotonic expansion.

In Friedmann's first paper of 1922, the metric equation for a positively curved space can easily be transformed by a change of coordinates into the Robertson-Walker form adopted today; but the one in
the second paper, describing a negatively curved space, is not at all
familiar, and it is not even obvious that, in this particular choice of
coordinates, the space really has a constant curvature.[3] Friedmann
actually used an old form of the metric of a space of constant curvature,
first given by Eugenio Beltrami. The coordinate transformation that
changes this metric into Robertson-Walker's unified form is "hideous,"
to apply Robertson's own words.[4]

While in the 1922 article Friedmann discussed in detail the time
development of his solutions, in the 1924 article he only indicates the
possibility of a non-stationary world with constant negative curvature

of space without going further. The reason is that the equations governing the evolution of the radius of the universe are similar to that of a world with constant positive spatial curvature if we change the curvature term to -1 instead of 1.

In his important conclusion, Friedmann prefers to discuss a problem never before tackled in cosmology: the global topology of space. This remarkable passage deserves to be reproduced in full:

> We turn ourselves to the discussion of the physical meaning of the result obtained in the preceding paragraphs. We have convinced ourselves that the Einstein world equations possess solutions that correspond to a world with constant negative curvature of space. This fact points out that the world equations taken alone are not sufficient to decide the question of the finiteness of our world. Knowledge of the curvature of space gives us still no immediate hint on its finiteness or infinitude. To arrive at a definite conclusion on the finiteness of space, one needs some supplementary agreements. Indeed we designate a space as finite, if the distance between two arbitrary non-coincident points of this space does not exceed a certain constant number, whatever pairs of points we might like to take. Consequently we must, before we tackle the problem of the finiteness of space, come to an agreement as to which points of this space we regard as different. If we, e.g., understand a sphere to be a surface of the three-dimensional euclidean space, we count the points that lie on the same circle of latitude and whose longitudes are different by just 360° as coincident; if we had in contrast considered these points as different, we would obtain a multiply-leafed spherical surface in euclidean space. The distance between arbitrary (two) points on a sphere does not exceed a finite number; if we, however, conceive of this sphere as an infinitely-many leafed surface, we can (by associating the points with different leaves in an appropriate manner) make this distance arbitrarily large. From this it becomes clear that before one goes into the considerations on the finiteness of space, one must be precise as to which points will be regarded as coincident and which as different.
>
> … As a criterion for the distinctness of points, [there] could serve, amongst others, the principle of "phantom anxiety."[5] By this

we mean the axiom that between every two different points one could draw only one straight (geodesic) line. If one accepts this principle, then one cannot regard two points which can be joined by more than one straight line as different. According to this principle, e.g., the two end points of the same diameter of a sphere are not different from each other.[6] Of course this principle excludes the possibility of phantoms, for the phantom appears at the same point as the image itself that is generating it.

The just discussed formulation of the concept of coincident and non-coincident points can lead to the picture... [where] spaces with positive constant curvature are finite.[7] However, the mentioned criterion does not allow us to conclude... [about] the finiteness of spaces of negative constant curvature. This is the reason therefore that, according to our opinion, Einstein's world equations without additional assumptions are not yet sufficient to draw a conclusion on the finiteness of our world.[8]

For Friedmann, the fundamental physical significance of his results is that "the world equations taken alone are not sufficient to decide the question of the finiteness of our world." He must have thought, like most physicists of the time, that only finite volume spaces (such as the hypersphere used by Einstein in his 1917 model) are physically admissible to describe real space. So far, the cosmological solutions of Einstein and de Sitter in 1917, and that of Friedmann in 1922, had a positive curvature and satisfied this criterion. With negatively curved spaces, the problem is more difficult: the natural prototype of a constant negatively curved space is a hyperbolic space of infinite volume. But Friedmann sees a loophole in the fact that Einstein's equations are not sufficient to decide whether the space is finite or infinite, even if the curvature is negative; additional assumptions must be made specifying boundary conditions, such as whether or not certain points in the space are identified with each other. The whole problem of cosmic topology was thus already posed, but Friedmann lacked a sufficient mathematical basis for further discussion: in 1924, the topological classification of Riemannian spaces was still non-existent. I will come back to the question in Chapter 17.

Einstein had no public reaction to Friedmann's second article. As we have seen, Friedmann passed away prematurely in September 1925, without having had the satisfaction of seeing the slightest acceptance of his cosmological ideas.

At the same time, another European scientist returned from the United States to teach at the University of Louvain. The young Belgian Georges Lemaître would independently take up the intuitions of the Russian scientist and amplify them until they became the basis of the modern Big Bang theory.

8. Georges Lemaître
(1894–1966)

Enclosed in a troubling duality
The man of faith and the researcher
Thus was Georges Lemaître's destiny
Canon of his state and great
Champion of astrophysics
Inveterate cosmologist author
Of a strict model of Universe
—André Verdet, "Hommages" (1984)[1]

UNLIKE FRIEDMANN, WHO ONLY CAME TO ASTRONOMY IN 1921–1922, three years before his death, Georges Lemaître was closely connected with astronomy throughout his long life. He always felt the absolute necessity to confront the facts of observation and theory. He was, for example, in his formative years much more aware than Friedmann of the experimental status of the theory of relativity.[2] At the same time, Lemaître was a remarkable mathematician, both in fundamental mathematics, with his work on quaternions or Störmer's problem, and in numerical analysis.[3] It should be noted that, unlike Friedmann, Lemaître had no affinity for the axiomatic approach to mathematics that was made fashionable by David Hilbert and the Göttingen school.

Lemaître was born on July 17, 1894, in Charleroi, Belgium.[4] The eldest child of a middle-class Catholic family, he was educated at the Jesuit college in his native town, and rapidly felt a call to become both a priest and a scientist. However, his father advised him that, before entering the seminary, he should complete his engineering studies. The young Lemaître followed his father's recommendation. At the age of seventeen he enrolled at the University of Louvain, where he studied engineering for three years. Just after he graduated, World War I burst out. He volunteered for the Belgian Infantry, mainly serving in artillery, and participated in important battles along the river Yser. During the war he began to read the work of mathematician Henri Poincaré. At the end of the war, he received one of the highest military distinctions.

It was in this military context that Georges Lemaître chose his dual scientific and religious vocations. "There were two ways to get to the truth, and I decided to take them both," he would later tell an American journalist.[5] Returning to his university studies in 1919, he changed his orientation, moving from engineering to the much more abstract physical and mathematical sciences under the supervision of the famous mathematician Charles de la Vallée Poussin. There he proved to be a major force. In 1920, he obtained his doctorate in mathematics (today corresponding to the Belgian bachelor of science or the American master's degree).

From this time on, Lemaître showed an open-mindedness and a diversity of interests that characterized him for the rest of his life: in parallel to his mathematical work, he obtained a bachelor's degree in Thomistic philosophy. Science did not represent everything for him. In the same year, 1920, Lemaître entered the seminary of Mechelen, at the Saint Rombaut House. The seminary was reserved for "late vocations." On September 23, 1923, he was ordained a priest by Cardinal Mercier, Archbishop of Mechelen and Primate of Belgium. His ecclesiastical training thus lasted only three years, instead of the six prescribed by canonical statutes.

During this period, Lemaître was preparing a dissertation on relativity and gravitation for a travel grant competition. He was obviously fascinated by Einstein's theory of general relativity which, in the 1920s, was practically unknown in the circles Lemaître frequented, and was only seriously studied by a small number of Belgian scientists, including Théophile de Donder (1872–1957). The latter, a former student of Poincaré, who had become a professor at the Université Libre de Bruxelles, studied inhomogeneous, spherically symmetrical

Figure 8.1.

Georges Lemaître (left) and his brother, Jacques, voluntarily enlisted in the Belgian army August 7, 1914, shortly after the outbreak of World War I.

solutions to Einstein's equations as early as 1920. In 1922, de Donder wrote a masterly treatise, *La gravifique einsteinienne*, and endeavored to translate general relativity into the language of variational principles.

Because Einstein's theory of general relativity was not at the time widely studied, Lemaître was forced to learn this difficult subject by himself, while being decisively influenced by the de Donder school. In

1922 he wrote a 131-page manuscript, *La physique d'Einstein*, which was not published until 1996, thirty years after his death.[6]

In July 1923, Lemaître obtained a scholarship from the Belgian government allowing him to study abroad. He spent the first year at the University of Cambridge, in the UK, studying stellar astronomy and general relativity with the famous astrophysicist Arthur Eddington.

Eddington (1882–1944) had been director of the Cambridge Observatory since 1914. During World War I, he obtained a copy of Einstein's articles, published in Berlin, through his Dutch colleague Willem de Sitter. He fully accepted the theory of general relativity, and made it known in England in 1918 through a report to the Physical Society of London on *The Relativity Theory of Gravitation*. As we have seen, Eddington then led the expedition to Principe Island in West Africa to measure the deflection of light rays during the 1919 solar eclipse. The following year, he wrote a layman's account of Einstein's gravitation theory, *Space, Time and Gravitation*, and in 1922, the technical book *The Mathematical Theory of Relativity*,[7] which Einstein considered "the finest presentation of the subject in any language."[8] Eddington described the cosmological models of Einstein and de Sitter, discussing the latter's prediction of a recession velocity of galaxies and the modest empirical support then available in observational data. At the same time, he conducted another line of fundamental research and published the results as a book in 1926, *The Internal Constitution of Stars*.

Lemaître had already carefully studied Eddington's work by the time he arrived in Cambridge, and the year he spent at his side only increased his admiration for him.[9] In a letter of recommendation dated December 24, 1924, addressed to de Donder, Eddington included a warm recommendation to his former student. "I found M. Lemaître a very brilliant student, wonderfully quick and clear-sighted, and of great mathematical ability," Eddington wrote. "He did some excellent work whilst here, which I hope he will publish soon. I hope he will do well with Shapley at Harvard. In case his name is considered for any post in Belgium I would be able to give him my strongest recommendations."[10]

Figure 8.2.

(top) Albert Einstein, Paul Ehrenfest, and Willem de Sitter; (bottom) Arthur Eddington and Hendrick Lorentz, at the office of de Sitter in Leiden, The Netherlands, September 26, 1923.

There followed a summer in Canada, including a four-week visit at the Dominion Observatory in British Columbia, after which, in September 1924, Lemaître arrived at the Harvard College Observatory. Here he began to work with Harlow Shapley on the nebulae problem. The term "nebula" had been used by astronomers for two centuries to refer to faint, cloud-like celestial objects that, unlike comets, do not change position or appearance. Shapley (1885–1972) had been appointed director of the Harvard College Observatory in 1921. At the time, his research focused mainly on the periodic variable stars (RR Lyrae stars and Cepheids), seeking to gauge distances and laying the foundations for estimating the distances of spiral nebulae.

Lemaître could not register as a graduate student at Harvard because the observatory had no teaching faculty, so he switched to MIT, where Edwin Hubble and Vesto Slipher were active. Hubble measured the distances of nebulae by observing variable Cepheid-type stars, while Slipher estimated their radial velocities from their spectral shifts. (See Chapter 9.)

The contrast between the research being conducted in Europe and in the United States was striking. As nebulae have very low brightness and require high quality observational data, their identification as possible galaxies outside our Milky Way required the use of large telescopes installed at exceptional sites. These did not exist in Europe, but they did exist in the United States, as Donald E. Osterbrock explains, partly because of the favorable climate and geography in some areas (the mountains of California and Arizona under often clear skies), and partly because of a few American science-loving millionaires, such as James Lick and Andrew Carnegie, who funded expensive projects.[11]

While closely following the experimental work of American astronomers, who were soon to found observational cosmology, Lemaître undertook a doctoral thesis at MIT with his compatriot Paul Heymans as advisor. His subject was the relativistic gravitational field inside a sphere filled with a non-homogeneous fluid—a subject suggested by Eddington. It was in fact a generalization to the inhomogeneous case of the famous 1916 inner Schwarzschild solution.

At the end of 1924 Lemaître attended the 33rd meeting of the American Astronomical Society in Washington, DC. It was there, on January 1, 1925, that Henry Norris Russell announced Edwin Hubble's discovery of Cepheids in spiral nebulae.[12] This made it possible to prove the existence of galaxies outside the Milky Way. Lemaître immediately understood that this new conception of "island universes" would have consequences for the theories of relativistic cosmology.

During his two-year stay in the United States, Lemaître visited important sites including the Lick, Mount Wilson (where he met Edwin Hubble and his night assistant Milton Humason), and Lowell observatories (where he met Slipher). There he got the best experimental data concerning the distances of nebulae (according to the Hubble school's data) as well as their velocities as deduced from their spectral shifts (Slipher's observations).

But on July 8, 1925, his American stay ended and Lemaître had to go back to Belgium. He immediately left Belgium, though, for the second general assembly of the Astronomical Union, held in Cambridge, England, July 14–22. In October, he was appointed lecturer at the Faculty of Science of Louvain, Belgium. On November 19, 1925, he submitted his doctoral thesis to MIT, titled "The Gravitational Field in a Fluid Sphere of Uniform Invariant Density according to the Theory of Relativity."[13] It was not accepted until December 15, 1926, after revision.

This work, it should be noted in passing, would eventually be developed as the important Lemaître-Tolman-Bondi metric. Lemaître discussed this non-homogeneous model with Richard Tolman at Caltech between November 1932 and January 1933, and Tolman used the model in his own publications. The model was often referred to as the Tolman model or the Tolman-Bondi model. But in 1997 Polish cosmologist Andrzej Krasinski corrected the historical record, calling it the Lemaître-Tolman model.[14]

In 1926–27, Lemaître went back to MIT, where he stayed during the third quarter of the academic year. Back in Europe in June 1927, he learned by mail that MIT had finally granted him his PhD in the physical sciences (he had been exempted from the oral defense). The same year, he was appointed professor at the University of Louvain and published his seminal article on the expanding universe and spectral shifts. (See Chapter 9.) He remained in this position until his retirement in 1964, sometimes interrupting his teaching for short stays abroad devoted to scientific contacts and conferences. He was chosen as a member of the Pontifical Academy of Sciences when it was created in 1936, became its president in March 1960, and remained so until his death in Louvain on June 20, 1966.

According to all the people who knew and worked with him—friends, students, collaborators—Lemaître had a very pleasant personality. His lectures were original if sometimes disorganized, and his students—whom he regularly took to a bakery to taste cakes—loved his kindness and his contagious laugh. Lemaître enjoyed music and played the piano remarkably well, particularly Bach and Chopin. He was interested in literature, and in the 1950s he wrote some manuscripts about Molière[15], arguing that the famous name disguised that of the true author (supposedly King Louis XIV!).[16] He also enjoyed photography and traveling and studied the Chinese language.[17]

In the chapters to follow we will consider Lemaître's conception of the relation between science and religion, and survey his exceptional contributions to cosmology, where he was a real pioneer. But to briefly summarize here, Lemaître's cosmology was built in two phases. In the first, Lemaître found independently of Friedmann that Einstein's equations admit non-static cosmological solutions. Simultaneously, he took into account American observations of galaxy velocities, to which he gave a physical meaning by interpreting them as clues to an expanding universe. In a second phase, Lemaître dared an even bolder hypothesis, which was in part a logical extension of the theory of the expanding universe. If the universe is expanding, he reasoned, in the past it had to have been much denser and, long ago, was condensed into a "primeval atom" whose successive splits have shaped it as it is now.

Reviewed and corrected over time, this conception became the theory of the Big Bang.

9. GALAXY RECESSION AND COSMIC EXPANSION (1927–1931)

Watch out follow live
With the strength of the fiery
The constant displacement
Towards the red of the spectrum
Distant stellars
From galaxies to nebulae
From nebulae to quasars
The unstoppable progression towards
The Non-Place, the Unobservable
Worlds already gone
—ANDRÉ VERDET, "HOMMAGES"[1]

AT THE BEGINNING OF THE 1920S, VERY FEW ASTRONOMERS accepted the existence of galaxies outside our own—that is, the "island universes" hypothesis proposed by Immanuel Kant and placed in doubt by William Huggins's discovery of intragalactic gaseous nebulae in 1864.[2] In particular, the Andromeda Nebula was generally considered to be but a solar system in formation rather than what it was later discovered to be, a large spiral galaxy in its own right, more than two million light years from our own spiral galaxy. In 1920 a "Great Debate" took place at the National Academy of Sciences in Washington, DC, intended to settle the question dividing the two camps. The one favorable to the view that the universe was filled with many galaxies was led by Heber Curtis. The other camp, holding to the view that there was just the one galaxy, was led by Harlow Shapley. The debate went unresolved for a lack of observations of sufficient quality[3]—that is, until an American astronomer made a startling discovery.

Observers and Theorists

It was 1924 when Edwin Hubble, working from Mount Wilson's Hooker telescope northeast of Los Angeles, identified Cepheids in the irregular nebula NGC 6822, in Messier 31 (the famous Andromeda Nebula) and Messier 33 (Triangle Nebula). He sent a paper describing his results to a meeting of astronomers in Washington. It was read by the General Secretary Henry Norris Russell on January 1, 1925, who concluded that "it confirms the island universe theory" and settled the Great Debate by demonstrating that spiral nebulae are other star systems analogous to our own galaxy, the Milky Way. Hubble received an award for his contribution, and in the same year published his final paper on NGC 6822,[4] making that galaxy the first object definitively assigned to a region outside our galactic system.[5] The following year, he published a lengthy paper on Messier 33 as an isolated system of stars and gaseous nebulae far beyond the limits of our galactic system.[6] By 1929 he reached the same conclusion about the Andromeda Galaxy.[7]

Although Georges Lemaître was primarily a remarkable mathematician and a theoretical physicist, unlike Einstein he wanted to stay closely related to astronomy and felt the absolute need for confronting both the observational data and the general relativity theory. This basic fact explains why as soon as 1927, while still a beginner in cosmology, he would be the first to understand the recent observations on the recession velocities of galaxies as a natural consequence of *dynamical* cosmological solutions of Einstein's field equations.[8]

Two years before, in 1925, Lemaître obtained his first notable scientific results, concerning the cosmological solution found by de Sitter. In 1923, Hermann Weyl had noted that test particles in de Sitter's universe move apart with velocities proportional to their mutual distances, but he did not provide an explicit coordinate system to prove his claims.[9] Other authors such as Carl Wirtz, Ludwig Silberstein, and Knut Lundmark had looked for a relation that fit de Sitter's static model (which, it should be noted in passing, was based on radial-velocity estimates that were later found to be considerably in error).[10] But it was Lemaître, then still a student, who, in two articles with the same title,[11] was the first to elucidate a possible link between de Sitter's universe and the redshifts of extragalactic nebulae.

Figure 9.1.
Georges Lemaître in 1925.

In the first article, Lemaître demonstrated how one could introduce new coordinates for the de Sitter universe that made the metric non-static, with a space of zero curvature and a scale factor depending exponentially on time. This metric would be used twenty years later by the keenest adversaries of the theory of the expanding universe in the framework of "steady-state models" (see Chapter 14), and still later in the 1980s to describe the hypothetical inflationary phase of the very early universe.[12]

In the second article, Lemaître deduced that the relation between the relative speed of test particles and their mutual distances in the de Sitter universe was linear. For the first time, the cosmological constant was allotted the role of a "cosmic repulsion" (when positive), forcing the worldlines of particles to recede with time. However, although Lemaître found this non-static feature promising, he also realized that, because of its connection to the redshifts of nebulae, the model resulted in an infinite euclidean space, a result he considered inadmissible: as a neo-Thomist he did not accept an actual infinity, and he would remain faithful to the finitude of space and matter throughout his career. Thus, he had to seek an alternative explanation to the de Sitter solution, one involving a truly non-static and spatially closed solution to Einstein's equations.

Receding Galaxies and an Expanding Universe

Since 1912, the American astronomer Vesto Slipher had undertaken a program of measuring the radial velocities of spiral nebulae.[13] The laws of light propagation imply that radiation is received with a different frequency from its emission frequency if the emitting source is in motion. Translated in terms of the Doppler-Fizeau effect, these frequency (or wavelength) shifts imply a radial velocity of the source relative to the observer. Radial velocities are measured by spectroscopy. The spectra of celestial objects (planets, stars, galaxies) contain dark lines that correspond to the radiation absorbed by the atoms *in situ*. The spectral lines of moving celestial objects are compared to those of the corresponding chemical elements at rest (i.e., in the laboratory), and the wavelength shift is related to the radial velocity of the source by a simple formula:

a redshift, i.e., towards the longest wavelengths, indicates the star is moving away, while a blueshift means it is getting closer.

In the 1910s Vesto Slipher had analyzed the spectra of twenty-five spiral nebulae that he had observed at Lowell Observatory in Flagstaff, Arizona; twenty-one of them displayed redshifts that could be interpreted as a systematic motion of recession (the exceptions were M81 and three galaxies from the Local Group).[14] Slipher presented his first results in August 1914 at the meeting of the American Astronomical Association at Northwestern University. At the end of his presentation he received a standing ovation. Particularly impressed was Danish astronomer Ejnar Hertzsprung, who during the period 1911–1913 had developed with Henry Norris Russell the relationship between the stars' absolute magnitudes or luminosities and their stellar classifications or effective temperatures (the so-called H-R diagram, a major step towards an understanding of stellar evolution), and then had begun to determine the distances of several Cepheid stars of our galaxy. In 1914 he wrote to Slipher, congratulating him on his "beautiful discovery of the great radial velocity of some spiral nebulae. It seems to me, that with this discovery the great question, if the spirals belong to the system of the Milky Way or not, is answered with great certainty to the end, that they do not."[15]

Slipher arrived at a similar conclusion. "It has for a long time been suggested that the spiral nebulae are stellar systems seen at great distances," he wrote in 1917. "This is the so-called 'island universe' theory, which regards our stellar system and the Milky Way as a great spiral nebula which we see from within. This theory, it seems to me, gains favor in the present observations."[16]

Some four years later, the following popular science article by Slipher appeared in the *New York Times* of January 19, 1921:

Dreyer Nebula no. 584 Inconceivably Distant

. . .

FLAGSTAFF, Ariz., Jan. 17.—The Lowell Observatory some years ago undertook to determine the velocity of the spiral nebulae—a thing that had not been previously attempted or thought possible.

The undertaking soon revealed the quite unexpected fact that spiral nebulae are far the most swiftly moving objects known in the heavens. A recent observation has shown that the nebula in the constellation Cetus, numbering 584 in Dreyer's catalogue, is one of very exceptional interest.

Like most spiral nebulae, this one is extremely faint, and to observe its velocity requires an exceedingly long photographic exposure with the most powerful instrumental equipment. This photograph was exposed from the end of December to the middle of January in order to give the weak light of the nebula's spectrum time to impress itself upon the plate. It is necessary to disperse the nebular light into a spectrum in order to observe the spectral lines, and to measure the amount they are shifted out of their normal positions, for it is this displacement of the nebula's lines that discloses and determines the velocity with which the nebula is itself moving.

The lines in its spectrum are greatly shifted, showing that the nebula is flying away from our region of space with a marvelous velocity of 1,100 miles per second.

This nebula belongs to the spiral family, which includes the great majority of the nebulae. They are the most distant of all celestial bodies, and must be enormously large.

If the above swiftly moving nebula be assumed to have left the region of the sun at the beginning of the earth, it is easily computed, assuming the geologists' recent estimate for the earth's age, that the nebula now must be many millions of light years distant.

The velocity of this nebula thus suggests a further increase to the estimated size of the spiral nebulae themselves as well as to their distances, and also further swells the dimensions of the known universe.[17]

The evidence for the redshifts continued to mount, mainly due to Slipher's efforts; by 1923 thirty-six of forty-one spiral nebulae displayed redshifts. However, nobody—not even Slipher himself—yet suspected the repercussions that these preliminary data would soon have for the whole of cosmology.

Curiously, Slipher never published his final list,[18] but it was provided in Arthur Eddington's book of 1923, *The Mathematical Theory of Relativity.* There Eddington noted, "One of the most perplexing problems in cosmogony is the great speed of the spiral nebulae. Their radial velocities average about 600 km. per sec. and there is a great preponderance of velocities of recession from the solar system."[19]

The influential British astronomer suggested that effects due to the curvature of space-time should be looked for and he referred to de Sitter's model for a possible explanation.

Thanks to Lemaître's various stays at Cambridge and MIT and his visits to the great American astronomical observatories of the time, Lemaître had met both Slipher and Hubble, and was perfectly informed of their preliminary results. As he wrote later: "In the spring of 1925, shortly before my return (to Belgium), I had the opportunity to attend a meeting of the Academy in Washington and to hear Hubble present the discovery of Cepheids in the Andromeda Nebula, which definitively established the distance of the Andromeda Nebula, and thus the general structure of the universe."[20]

But Lemaître was more than a dogged collector of the latest astronomical data. With the new data in hand, he set about to build a new cosmological solution to Einstein's equations.

In 1927, he published his fundamental article, "Un univers homogène de masse constante et de rayon croissant, rendant compte de la vitesse radiale des nébuleuses extragalactiques" ("A homogeneous universe of constant mass and increasing radius, accounting for the radial velocity of extragalactic nebulae"). As the title of the article made clear, Lemaître was connecting the idea of space itself expanding, an idea arising naturally from the non-static cosmological solutions of general relativity, with the observations of the recession velocities of extragalactic nebulae. He was the first to do so.

The article begins by comparing de Sitter's model of the universe with Einstein's. The de Sitter model ignored the existence of matter; however, it emphasized the recession velocities of spiral nebulae as a simple consequence of the gravitational field. Einstein's solution allowed for the presence of matter and led to a relation between matter density and the radius of the space—assumed to be a positively curved hypersphere. Being strictly static due to an adjustment of the cosmological constant, it could not, however, explain the recession of the galaxies. Lemaître thus looked for a new solution to the relativistic equations, combining the advantages of the Einstein and de Sitter models without their inconveniences. Or to put it positively, Lemaître's model makes room for matter and, at the same time, explains the recession velocities.

He assumes a positively curved space (as made clear in a footnote, with "elliptic topology," namely that of the projective space $\mathbf{P}^3$ obtained by identification of antipodal points of the simply connected hypersphere $\mathbf{S}^3$) with the radius of curvature R and consequently the matter density ρ being functions of time t, and a non-zero cosmological constant λ. From Einstein's field equations he obtains differential equations for $R(t)$ and $\rho(t)$ almost identical to those previously obtained by Friedmann (though Lemaître apparently was not aware of Friedmann's work; see below). The difference is that Lemaître supposes the conservation of energy—this is the first introduction of thermodynamics into relativistic cosmology—and he incorporates the pressure of radiation as well as the matter density into the stress-energy tensor. (He rightly considers the matter pressure to be negligible.)

Lemaître emphasizes the importance of radiation pressure in the first stages of the cosmic expansion. Now it is well known that, within the framework of Big Bang models, the approximation of zero pressure (known as "dust") is valid only for approximately four hundred thousand years after the Big Bang. Just like Einstein and de Sitter, Friedmann had assumed that the term of pressure in the stress-energy tensor was always zero. The equations derived by Lemaître are thus more general and realistic.

Lemaître shows how the Einstein and de Sitter models are particular solutions of the general equations. Next, he chooses as initial conditions $R' = R'' = 0$, $R = R_0$ at $t = -\infty$, and he adjusts the value of the cosmological constant such that $\lambda = 1/R_0$, in the same way Einstein had adjusted the value of λ in his static model with constant radius R_0.

As a consequence, the exact solution $t = f(R)$ that Lemaître obtains (equation 30 of the article) describes a monotonically expanding universe, which, when one goes back indefinitely in time, approaches in an asymptotic way Einstein's static solution, while in the future it approaches asymptotically an exponentially expanding de Sitter universe.

This model, without an initial singularity and, consequently, not possessing a definite age—like the "monotonic solution of second species" found earlier by Friedmann—would later be dubbed the Eddington-Lemaître model.

Lemaître does not provide a graph for $R(t)$ but does give numerical values in a table going from $t = -\infty$ to $t = +\infty$. For the sake of clarity, the figure below depicts such a graph.

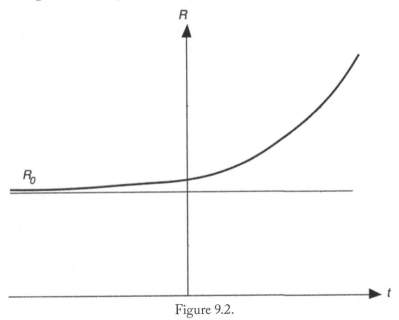

Figure 9.2.

Lemaître's 1927 universe model, later named the Eddington–Lemaître model. The radius R_0 of the static Einstein hypersphere is reached asymptotically for $t = -\infty$. The origin of cosmic time is arbitrary; thus the model does not pose any problem of age.

Lemaître conceived the static Einstein universe as a kind of pre-universe out of which the expansion had grown as a result of an instability. As a physical cause for the expansion he suggested the radiation pressure itself, due to its infinite accumulation in a closed static universe, but he did not develop this (erroneous) idea.

While giving his preference to this particular model in his article, Lemaître nevertheless calculated the whole of dynamical homogeneous cosmological solutions, since he had the general formula (equation 11) making it possible to calculate the time evolution of all the homogeneous isotropic models with positive curvature. The Lemaître archives at the University of Louvain include a red pad with the inscription "1927," which contains the galley proofs of his article, some notes in handwriting connected with the paper, and two diagrams which (unfortunately) do not appear in any of his publications. These diagrams depict the time evolution of the space scale factor depending on the value of the cosmological constant for all homogeneous and isotropic solutions of Einstein's equations with positive curvature of space; see the figure below.

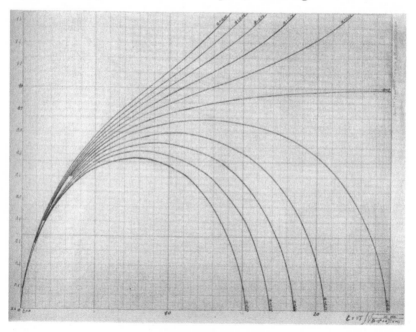

Figure 9.3.

Handwritten graph by Lemaître. This extraordinary diagram, plotted by Lemaître in 1927 but unpublished until 1998,[21] depicts the time evolution of the radius of the universe with the cosmological constant (denoted a), for a space of positive curvature. All the models start with a singularity at ($x = 0$, $t = 0$). For a sufficiently large cosmological constant a, the universe becomes open. The most recent cosmological data are compatible with Lemaître's solution with positive curvature and accelerated expansion (top curve).

As mentioned above, the 1927 article does not refer to the work of Friedmann, published in *Zeitschrift für Physik*—although that was one of the best-known journals in theoretical physics at the time. This omission seems strange if one remembers the two notes by Einstein published in the same journal (see Chapter 5), which had been widely discussed in the scientific community. A plausible explanation is that Lemaître could not read the German.[22] Friedmann's articles were pointed out to Lemaître by Einstein himself, during their meeting at the 1927 Solvay Conference. Lemaître's first reference to Friedmann thus appears in a 1929 article written in French, "La grandeur de l'espace,"[23] in which Lemaître thanks "Mr. Einstein for the kindness that he showed by announcing to me the important work of Friedmann, which includes several of the results contained in my note on a homogeneous universe." The reference would also appear in the 1931 English translation of Lemaître's article (see below).

Lemaître's work is notable for providing the first interpretation of cosmological redshifts as a natural effect of the expansion of the universe within the framework of general relativity, instead of attributing it to the real motion of galaxies. As it is given in equation 23—$R'/R = v/cr$—space is constantly expanding and consequently increases the apparent separations between galaxies. This idea would prove to be one of the most profound discoveries of our time.

The proportional relation between the recession velocity v and the distance r is an approximation valid at not too large distances which can be used, he writes, "within the limits of the visible spectrum." Then, using the available astronomical data, Lemaître calculates the relation in equation 24, with a factor 625 or 575 km/s/Mpc (which means that galaxies that are 1 megaparsec away have a recession speed of 625 or 575 km/sec). Depending on the choice of observations, this presented an enormous scatter:

> Using the 42 extra-galactic nebulae in the Hubble and Strömberg lists, and taking into account the Sun's own speed, we find an average distance of 0.95 million parsecs and a radial velocity of 600 km/s, or 625 km/s at 10^6 parsecs. We will therefore adopt $R'/R = v/rc = 0.68 \times 10^{-27}$ cm^{-1} (equation 24).

For this the Belgian scientist uses a list of forty-two radial velocities compiled by Gustav Strömberg,[24] a Swedish astronomer at the
Mount Wilson Observatory, and deduces the distance of the corresponding extra-galactic nebulae from an empirical formula relating
the distance and the absolute magnitude provided by Hubble, who
himself took the magnitudes from Hopmann.[25] This was the first
calculation of the so-called Hubble law and the Hubble constant, to
be recognized only much later.

Eventually, Lemaître was able to give the numerical figures for
the initial and present-day values of the radius of the universe, respectively $R_0 = 2.7 \times 10^8\ pc$ and $R = 6 \times 10^9\ pc$. At the very end he points
out that the largest part of the universe will be forever out of reach
of the visible spectrum, since the maximum distance reached by the
Mt. Wilson telescope is only $R/120$, whereas for a distance greater
than $R/115$, the whole visible spectrum is displaced into the infrared.
Lemaître could not imagine our present-day era with infrared and
submillimeter telescopes placed on board satellites.

We have seen above that Lemaître already knew all the solutions
to Einstein's equations for homogeneous and isotropic universes. The
reason he privileged a very particular model, adjusting the cosmological constant in order to have no beginning of time, is that he
overestimated the proportionality factor—later called the Hubble
constant. The latter gives an order of magnitude of the duration of the
expansion phase. With the estimate of about 600 km/s/Mpc found
by Lemaître, this period is only about one billion years, a number
less than the age of the Earth as estimated by geologists at the time.
Thus, the model with exponential expansion and no beginning allowed Lemaître to reconcile his theory with both astronomical and
geological data.

First Reactions

The significance of Lemaître's work remained mostly unnoticed for
three years. A reason commonly given is that it was published not
in one of the prestigious astronomical journals of the time but in
French and in a journal that has been characterized as obscure and

inaccessible.[26] There is a grain of truth in this explanation, but as D. Lambert has rightly pointed out, the journal in question, *Annales de la Société Scientifique de Bruxelles*, published some articles in English, was of an excellent scientific level, and therefore was included in a large number of academic libraries and observatories around the world. Moreover, a much larger scientific audience then than today could read French.[27] Rather, the main obstacle to a larger diffusion of Lemaître's article was that most of the physicists of the time, such as Einstein and Hubble, could not accept the idea of a non-static universe. This was not the case with Eddington. Unfortunately, his former mentor, to whom Lemaître had sent a copy, either forgot to read it in time or failed to understand its importance.

From October 24–29, 1927, the Fifth Solvay Conference in Physics took place in Brussels, one of the great meetings of world science. The Solvay Conference was devoted to the new discipline of quantum mechanics, whose problems disturbed many physicists. Among them was Einstein. For Lemaître, it was the opportunity to meet and talk with the father of general relativity. He later reported on this meeting:

> While walking in the alleys of the Parc Léopold, [Einstein] spoke to me about an article, little noticed, which I had written the previous year on the expansion of the universe and which a friend had made him read. After some favorable technical remarks, he concluded by saying that from the physical point of view that appeared completely abominable to him. As I sought to prolong the conversation, Auguste Piccard, who accompanied him, invited me to go up by taxi with Einstein, who was to visit his laboratory at the University of Brussels. In the taxi, I spoke about the speeds of nebulae and I had the impression that Einstein was hardly aware of the astronomical facts.[28]

André Deprit, a former student of Lemaître, gave a more picturesque and slightly different version of this encounter:

> Einstein had been invited to discuss his deterministic conception of the world with the young pioneers of quantum mechanics;

Lemaître was pacing up and down in front of the Institute, hoping to hook him on the way. While it's true that Professor Piccard, who was escorting Einstein that afternoon, picked Lemaître up in the taxi, the fact remains that Lemaître felt spurned. Yes, Einstein had read the note that had just appeared in the *Annales de la Société Scientifique*; the mathematics were correct, but the physics of the article, what an abomination! Need one say more? To defend himself, Lemaître mumbled a discreet allusion to Hubble's observations in English, which he withdrew immediately so as not to embarrass Professor Piccard, as he understood that Einstein was not aware of them. The conversation stopped for a moment, and Piccard resumed it with Einstein, but in German: Lemaître, who knew no German, had no choice but to remain silent.[29]

Einstein's response to Lemaître shows the same unwillingness to change his position that characterized his former response to Friedmann: he accepted the mathematics, but not a physically expanding universe. According to D. Lambert, this reaction came from the fact that Einstein's implicit philosophy was inspired by Spinoza.[30] For the Dutch philosopher, "God" (*Deus*) was identified with "Nature" (*Natura*): "*Deus sive Natura*." Consequently, due to the immutability of God, one could not accept any motion or evolution of Nature itself.[31] Einstein thus rejected the idea of an evolving universe, i.e., a world with a real history. This "theological" prejudice led him also to criticize strongly the idea of expanding (and contracting) universes put forward by Friedmann and Lemaître.

In July 1928, Lemaître went to Leiden, where de Sitter presided over the third assembly of the International Astronomical Union, but did not meet him. The hour of the Big Bang had obviously not yet come.

The same year H. P. Robertson published an article seeking to replace de Sitter's metric with a "mathematically equivalent [metric] in which many of the apparent paradoxes inherent in [de Sitter's solution] were eliminated."[32] He got the formula $v = cd/R$ where d is the distance of the nebula and R the radius of curvature of the universe, but in the framework of a *static* solution. Robertson used the same set of observations that Lemaître used (though he did not know of Lemaître's articles of 1925 and 1927) and that Hubble would later use. From this he calculated $R = 2 \times 10^{27}$ cm and a proportionality constant of 464 km/s/Mpc.[33] In a trailblazing article the following year,[34] Robertson related his detailed search for all the mathematical models satisfying a spatially homogeneous and isotropic universe and that also imply strong symmetries in the solutions to Einstein's equations.

In 1929, Hubble used the experimental data on the Doppler redshifts, mostly given by Slipher, and found a linear velocity-distance relation $v = Hr$ with $H = 465 \pm 50$ km/s/Mpc for twenty-four objects and 513 ± 60 km/s/Mpc for nine groups.[35] The law was strictly identical to Lemaître's equation 24, with almost the same proportionality factor.

However, Hubble did not take the crucial step to expanding-universe models. He stated, "The outstanding feature, however, is the possibility that the velocity-distance relation may represent the de Sitter effect."[36] In the introduction to his 1936 book, *The Realm of Nebulae*, Hubble discussed the interface between observation and theory, and honestly stated, "The author of this book is primarily an observer."[37] In fact, out of the 202 pages in the book, he discusses the theoretical interpretation of his observations only on page 198, in a last paragraph entitled "Theories of Cosmology."[38] He makes no mention of the work of Lemaître, but quotes Friedmann, Robertson, and Arthur Milne (who attempted a Newtonian explanation with his theory of "kinematic relativity"). Moreover, Hubble makes the mistake of considering the spectral shift as a pure Doppler effect (due to the galaxies' own recession velocity) and not as an expansion effect (increase of the space scale radius over time).

And all during his life he would remain skeptical about the general relativistic interpretation of his observations. As his biographer G. Christianson has pointed out, Hubble was chary of "all theories of cosmic expansion long after most astronomers and physicists had been won over. When queried about the matter as late as 1937, he sounded like an incredulous schoolboy: 'Well, perhaps the nebulae are all receding in this peculiar manner. But the notion is rather startling.'"[39]

Indeed, the idea that the expansion of the universe was discovered by Hubble is a myth that was first propagated by his collaborator Milton Humason as early as 1931[40] and by Hubble himself. Fiercely territorial, Hubble wrote in a letter to de Sitter, dated August 21, 1930: "I consider the velocity-distance relation, its formulation, testing and confirmation, as a Mount Wilson contribution and I am deeply concerned in its recognition as such."[41]

Only one month after Hubble's article, Tolman joined the game of searching for an explanation of recession velocities, but still in the framework of a static solution, as he said:

> The correlation between distance and apparent radial velocity of the extra-galactic nebulae obtained by Hubble, and the recent measurement of the Doppler effect for a very distant nebula made by Humason at the Mount Wilson Observatory, make it desirable to consider once more the theoretical relations between distance and Doppler effect which could be expected from the form of line element for the universe proposed by de Sitter.[42]

One year later, Tolman published another article in which he suggested that the expansion was due to the conversion of matter into radiation, a mistaken idea already proposed by Lemaître in his 1927 article.[43] The latter was again not quoted.

A new opportunity for the recognition of Lemaître's model arose in early 1930. In January, in London, a discussion between Eddington and de Sitter took place at a meeting of the Royal Astronomical Society. They did not know how to interpret the data on the recession velocities of galaxies. Eddington suggested that the problem could be due to the fact that only static models of the universe were hitherto considered; he nicely formulated the situation as follows: "Shall we put a little motion into Einstein's world of inert matter, or shall we put a little matter into de Sitter's Primum Mobile?"[44] He called for new searches in order to explain the recession velocities in terms of dynamical space models.

Having read the report of the meeting in London, Lemaître understood that Eddington and de Sitter posed a problem that he had already solved. He thus wrote to Eddington to point out his 1927 article and requested that Eddington send a copy to de Sitter:

Dear Professor Eddington, I have just read the February n° of the *Observatory* and your suggestion of investigating non-statical intermediary solutions between those of Einstein and de Sitter. I made these investigations two years ago. I consider a universe of curvature constant in space but increasing with time. And I emphasize the existence of [a] solution in which the motion of the nebulae is always [a] receding one from time minus infinity to plus infinity.[45]

Lemaître continued:

I had occasion to speak of the matter with Einstein two years ago. He told me that the theory was right and is all which needs to be done, that it was not new but had been considered by Friedmann. He made [criticisms] against [it,] which he was obliged to withdraw, but [said] that from the physical point of view it was *tout fait abominable*.[46]

Eddington was one of the most prominent figures of science at the time and was in the best possible position to play a key role in obtaining recognition for Lemaître's results. This time he paid attention to his former student's contribution. He made apologies and dispatched a copy to de Sitter in Holland and Shapley in the United States. Eddington was somewhat embarrassed, according to George McVittie, at the time a research student of Eddington's, working with him on the stability of Einstein's static model. McVittie wrote that he remembered "the day when Eddington, rather shamefacedly, showed me a letter from Lemaître which reminded Eddington of the solution to the problem which Lemaître had already given. Eddington confessed that although he had seen Lemaître's paper in 1927 he had forgotten completely about it until that moment."[47]

On March 19, Eddington sent Lemaître's paper to de Sitter in Leiden with the following comment:

It was the report of your remarks and mine at the [Royal Astronomical Society] which caused Lemaître to write to me about it. At this time, one of my research students, McVittie, and I had been worrying at the problem and made considerable progress; so it was a blow to us to find it was done much more completely by Lemaître (a blow attenuated, as far as I am concerned, by the fact that Lemaître was a student of mine).[48]

De Sitter answered Lemaître very favorably in a letter dated March 25, 1930:

My Dear Colleague

A few days ago Mr. Eddington sent me a copy of your small but important 1927 [article] "A Homogeneous Universe of Constant Mass and Increasing Radius," which I read with the greatest interest and admiration. I had myself, for several weeks, tried to find a formula for ds^2 that would include the two solutions that I called A and B in my communication to the R.A.S. of 1917 as special cases, but I had not succeeded. I had, among other things, found the solution that I later encountered in Levi-Civita's book (*The Absolute Differential Calculus*), p. 425–436, but which seems to me impossible from a physical point of view.

Your solution, simple and elegant, seems to me entirely satisfactory—if we can accept your assumption $V\delta$ = constant. The mass $M = V\delta$ is the material mass—Eddington's ρ_0 (mass invariant)—and can it remain invariant?

Stars radiate energy continuously, and probably the amount of energy radiated during the life of a star like the sun is of the same order as its mass. There must be radiation pressure in the universe, and I don't think it is negligible. But I have found that the solution of your equations by taking $\beta > 0$ is not essentially different from the one you give for $\beta = 0$.

I am currently preparing a paper on the distance of nebulae (containing the research I talked about in London in January, see the "Observatory"), and I will add a note on your solution, if I may.

Please believe, dear colleague, in my most distinguished sentiments.

W. de Sitter[49]

Lemaître replied to the Dutch physicist on April 5, explaining why the radiation pressure (given by $1/R^4$ in de Sitter's notation) seemed to him to play a negligible role in the expansion of the universe, and confessing that he had since learned of Friedmann's pioneering work from Einstein himself:

Thank you very much for your interest in my note on the variable radius universe and for your offer to devote a note to it in the dissertation you are preparing. I await with great interest the clarifications you have obtained on the relationship between v and r and the diagrams you have shown to the members of the R.A.S.

About the importance of the radiation pressure in the universe, I think it cannot be considerable....

The variable-radius universe was considered by Friedman according to the same equations that I came to later, but without reference to astronomical phenomena. He does not insist on the double root solution, but discusses the elliptic integral and classifies the solutions into

Monotone Welt erster Art → R varying from 0 to ∞
Monotone Welt zweiter Art → R varying from R_0 to ∞
Periodische Welt → R varying between 0 and a maximum
The solution I have specified is the common borderline case of these three classes of universe.

I was not aware of this dissertation when I wrote my article. It was later brought to my attention by Einstein. I mentioned it at a popularization conference on *"La grandeur de l'espace"* (*Revue des questions scientifiques* T.XV 1929 pp. 189 to 218) of which I will send you a separate extract soon.

In late May, de Sitter published a discussion about the expansion of the universe, where he wrote:

A dynamical solution of the equations (4) with the line-element (5) (7) and the material energy tensor (6) is given by Dr. G. Lemaître in a paper published in 1927, which had unfortunately escaped my notice until my attention was called to it by Professor Eddington a few weeks ago.[50]

For his part, Eddington reworked his communication to the following meeting of the Royal Astronomical Society in May, to introduce Lemaître's ideas on dynamical universes.[51] Around the same time, he also published an important article in which he reexamined Einstein's static model and discovered that, like a pen balanced on its point, it was unstable: any slight disturbance in the equilibrium would start the increase of the radius of the hypersphere; then he adopted Lemaître's model of an expanding universe—which would henceforward be referred to as the Eddington-Lemaître model—and calculated that the original size of the universe as conceived by Einstein was about 1,200 million light years, of the same order of magnitude as that estimated by Lemaître.[52] Interestingly, Eddington also considered the possibility of an initial universe with a mass M greater or smaller than the mass M_E of the Einstein model. But he rejected the two solutions, arguing that, for $M > M_E$, "it seems to require a sudden and peculiar beginning of things," whereas for $M < M_E$, "the date of the beginning of the universe is uncomfortably recent."

Eventually, Eddington sponsored the English translation of Lemaître's 1927 article for publication in the *Monthly Notices of the Royal Astronomical Society*.[53]

Figure 9.4.
Portrait of English astronomer and physicist Arthur Eddington.

With the support of Eddington and de Sitter, Lemaître suddenly rose to the status of a celebrated scientific innovator. He was invited to London to take part in a meeting of the British Association on the relation between the physical universe and spirituality. But in the meantime, he had progressed considerably in his investigations of relativistic cosmologies, and instead of promoting his model of 1927, he dared to propose an even more revolutionary idea, one that precipitated another paradigm shift in cosmology,[54] which we will take up in the next two chapters.

The English Translation and Discrepancies

A great deal has been written on the topic of who really discovered the expanding universe.[55] The French astronomer Paul Couderc[56] was probably the first to rightly underline the priority of Lemaître over Hubble, but since Lemaître himself never claimed any priority, the question was not much discussed.[57]

An intriguing discrepancy between the original French article and its English translation has been cited by various authors:[58] an important paragraph was replaced by a single sentence. In the original paragraph, Lemaître discussed the observational data and equation 24, giving the relation of proportionality between the recession velocity and the distance, and including the determination of the constant that later became known as Hubble's constant. The short replacement said only, "From a discussion of available data, we adopt $R'/R = 0.68 \times 10^{-27} cm^{-1}$."

It is curious that the crucial paragraphs assessing the so-called "Hubble law" were dropped, and some astronomers and historians of science have speculated about the reasons for the deletions, and even about the identity of the author of the translation (generally assumed to be Eddington). For the very good reason that Lemaître was the first to explain what is now known as Hubble's law, they have come to suspect, without any material evidence, that Lemaître or his translator was pressured to give Hubble priority in the derivation of the law $v=Hr$. As a consequence, Lemaître was not recognized as the discoverer of the expansion of the universe. In fact, to this day multitudes of textbooks and articles in the popular media proclaim Hubble as the discoverer of the expanding universe, although Hubble himself never believed in such an explanation!

In 2011, accusations flared up against Hubble.[59] There was suspicion that the editor of the *Monthly Notices of the Royal Astronomical Society*, possibly at Hubble's own behest, had censored Lemaître.[60] The suspicion was based on the "complex personality" of the American astronomer, who strongly desired to be credited with determining the Hubble constant.

The controversy was soon put to rest by Mario Livio of the Space Telescope Institute.[61] Combined research by Liliane Moens, the curator of the *Archives Georges Lemaître* at Louvain; Peter Hingley, the librarian of the Royal Astronomical Society in London; and Bob Carswell, the editor-in-chief of the *Monthly Notices*, showed that on February 17, 1931, Lemaître received a letter from William Smart, editor of the *Monthly Notices of the Royal Astronomical Society*, proposing, on behalf of the Council of the Royal Astronomical Society, of which Eddington was a member, that Lemaître publish an English translation of his 1927 paper and become a fellow of this prestigious society. In the letter, Smart also proposed some modifications if Lemaître wished to make them:

> Dear Dr. Lemaître,
>
> At the R.A.S. Council meeting last Friday it was resolved to ask you if you would allow your paper "Un univers homogène..." in the *Annales de la Soc. Sci. de Bruxelles* to be reprinted in the *Monthly Notices*. It has been felt that it was not circulated as widely—or isn't as well known—as its importance warrants, especially in English-speaking countries. This request of the Council is almost unique in the Society's annals and it shows you how much the Society would appreciate the honour of giving your paper a greater publicity amongst English-speaking scientists. Briefly—if the Soc. Scientifique de Bruxelles is also willing to give its permission—we should prefer the paper translated into English. Also, if you have any further additions etc. on the subject, we would gladly print these too. I suppose that if there were additions a note could be inserted to the effect that §§1–n are substantially from the Brussels paper and

the remainder is new (or something more elegant). Personally and also on behalf of the Society I hope that you will be able to do this.

By the way, you are not a fellow of the Society: if you would like to become a fellow, would you let me know and Eddington and I will sign your nomination paper.

Lemaître's response of March 9, 1931:

Dear Dr. Smart,

I highly appreciate the honour for me and for our society to have my 1927 paper reprinted by the Royal Astronomical Society. I send you a translation of the paper. I did not find [it] advisable to reprint the provisional discussion of radial velocities which is clearly of no actual interest, and also the geometrical note, which could be replaced by a small bibliography of ancient and new papers on the subject. I join a French text with indication of the passages omitted in the translation. I made this translation as exact as I can, but I would be very glad if some of yours would be kind enough to read it and correct my English which I am afraid is rather rough. No formula is changed, and even the final suggestion which is not confirmed by recent work of mine has not been modified. I did not write again the table which may be printed from the French text.

As regards to addition[s] on the subject, I just obtained the equations of the expanding universe by a new method which makes clear the influence of the condensations and the possible causes of the expansion. I would be very glad to have them presented to your society as a separate paper.

I would like very much to become a fellow of your society and would appreciate to be presented by Prof. Eddington and you.

If Prof. Eddington has yet a reprint of his May paper in MN [manuscript] I would be very glad to receive it.

Will you be kind enough to present my best regards to Prof. Eddington.

Lemaître translated his own article, and he chose to delete several paragraphs and notes. There was no external pressure to do so: he simply felt that the data used in 1927 had become obsolete compared to those published in the meantime by Hubble in 1929 (which differed only slightly).[62] This choice by Lemaître is quite comprehensible because the 1927 data gave only very imperfectly the linear relation $v = Hd$, whereas in 1931 the new data from Hubble allowed him to validate this relationship in a much more precise manner. (See Figure 9.5 for comparative plots.) Also, as he himself later explained (in 1950), in 1927 he did not have at his disposal data concerning clusters of galaxies, and he added that "Hubble's law could not be proved without the knowledge of the clusters of galaxies."[63]

Here we find again one of the characteristic features of Lemaître's personality, namely the crucial importance he always gave to the most recent experimental data. For instance, in a manuscript for a Japanese encyclopedia written just before World War II, he adopted "The best value (of the Hubble ratio) according to recent discussion by Knox, Show and Stabley (that) seems to be 405 km/sec/megaparsec."

We see also that William Smart proposed to Lemaître that he add comments rather than remove them. But the Belgian scientist, who in fact had radically new ideas, preferred to write a new paper, "The Expanding Universe," which was published in the same issue of the journal, just following the adapted translation of his 1927 paper (see Chapter 11). Thus, far from appearing to be an instrument of censorship, Smart's letter was an invitation to Lemaître to spread his latest ideas freely.

Lemaître's preoccupations had changed since 1927; the question that occupied him in 1931 was less that of the expansion of the universe than that of the deep cause of the expansion and of the "natural" beginning of the universe, or even that of the formation of galaxies in an expanding universe. The same year when his vision of a dynamic universe was to be accepted by the scientific community, including Eddington, de Sitter, and Einstein, Lemaître dared to make a much more outrageous assumption: If the universe is expanding now, must it not have been much smaller and denser at some time in the past? Instead of considering Einstein's static model as an initial stage from which the dynamic model started, is it not more logical to think of the universe as starting its expansion from an extremely small and condensed state, governed by quantum processes? Between Lemaître and his colleagues there thus emerged another controversy, which would not be resolved in his lifetime: that of the very birth of the universe.

Before concluding, it should be mentioned that Lemaître's request to join the Royal Astronomical Society, at Smart's invitation, was eventually granted. He was elected as an associate on May 12, 1939.

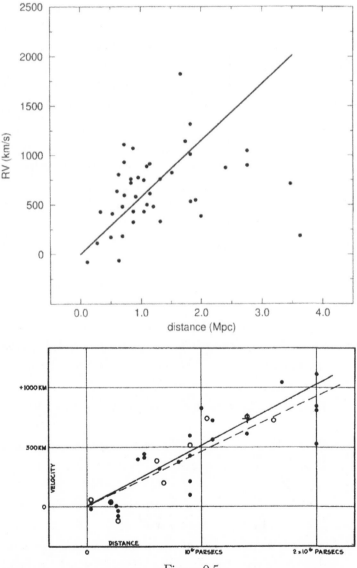

Figure 9.5.

Comparison between the data used by Lemaître in 1927 (top) to yield the first empirical value of the rate of expansion of the universe as 575 km/s/Mpc, and the radial velocity–distance diagram published by Hubble in 1929, with a best slope of 530 km/s/Mpc (bottom).[64]

Late Recognition

The fact remains that Lemaître had predicted and calculated as early as 1927 what Hubble had empirically rediscovered in 1929. Lemaître's letter to Smart also provides an insight into the scientific psychology of (some of) the scientists of the 1920s, and emphasizes another characteristic feature of Lemaître's personality, one that could be said to contrast sharply with that of his American "rival": modesty.

Here we want to be careful. "There is a view that Hubble was not generous in acknowledging the contributions of others," writes Ken Freeman. "Some who knew him regarded him poorly in this respect. On the other hand, some of us are careless about picking up ideas and forgetting where they came from. It still happens. Geography, institutional rivalry and culture may also be significant elements in this behavior." But for others, modesty and generosity of spirit appear to predominate over the desire for credit.[65] That was clearly the case with Georges Lemaître. For example, always careful to cite the work of his colleagues, his 1931 translation of his 1927 paper not only spotlights Hubble's velocity–distance diagram from 1929 but also provides at the end new references to other material that could not be given in the 1927 article: Friedmann's article of 1922 and Einstein's comments on it, Tolman's article about models of variable radius of 1930, the developments of his own model given by Eddington, de Sitter, and himself in 1930, and two popular expositions he gave in 1929 (in French) and one by de Sitter in 1931.

Most importantly, and as Mario Livio explains, "Lemaître was not at all obsessed with establishing priority for his original discovery."[66] In his articles and lectures after the Second World War, Lemaître often cited Hubble's law, but never mentioned his own pioneering contribution of 1927.[67]

In 1950, the French astronomer Paul Couderc published a bestselling book in which Lemaître was for the first time in history credited with the discovery of the expansion of the universe.[68] Lemaître found it overly complimentary and wrote a review in which he stated:

> About my contribution of 1927, I do not want to discuss if I was a professional astronomer. I was, in any event, an IAU member

(Cambridge, 1925), and I had studied astronomy for two years, a year with Eddington and another year in U.S. observatories. I visited Slipher and Hubble and heard [Hubble] in Washington, in 1925, making his memorable communication about the distance [to] the Andromeda nebula. While my mathematics bibliography was seriously lacking since I did not know the work of Friedmann, it was perfectly up to date from the astronomical point of view; I calculated [in my contribution] the coefficient of expansion (575 km per sec per megaparsecs, 625 with a questionable statistical correction). Of course, before the discovery and study of clusters of nebulae, there was no point to establishing the Hubble law, but only to calculating its coefficient. The title of my note leaves no doubt on my intentions: "A Universe with a constant mass and increasing radius as an explanation of the radial velocity of extra-galactic nebulae." I apologize if all of this is too personal. But, as noted by the author (p. 161), "the history of this science competition is not irrelevant" and it is useful to highlight the details to enable an exact understanding of the scope of the argument that can be drawn from this.[69]

The last sentence shows that, modesty aside, and as David Block argues, "Lemaître clearly did not want the rich fusion of theory and observations contained in his 1927 paper to be buried in the sands of time."[70]

In any event, the controversy, resolved by Mario Livio, has had an interesting effect: a resolution was proposed at the Thirtieth International Astronomical Union General Assembly, held in Vienna in 2018, "on a suggested renaming of the Hubble Law," to be decided by an electronic vote open to the entire community of IAU members. I reproduce here the full text of the resolution:

> Resolution B4 on a suggested renaming of the Hubble Law proposed by the IAU Executive Committee
>
> The XXXth General Assembly of the International Astronomical Union, considering
>   1. that the discovery of the apparent recession of the galaxies, which is usually referred to as the "Hubble law," is one of the major

milestones in the development of the science of astronomy during the last hundred years and can be considered one of the founding pillars of modern cosmology;

2. that the Belgian astronomer Georges Lemaître, in 1927, published (in French) the paper entitled "Un Univers homogène de masse constante et de rayon croissant rendant compte de la vitesse radiale des nébuleuses extra-galactiques." In this he first rediscovered Friedman's dynamic solution to Einstein's general relativity equations that describes an expanding universe. He also derives that the expansion of the universe implies the spectra of distant galaxies are redshifted by an amount proportional to their distance. Finally he uses published data on the velocities and photometric distances of galaxies to derive the rate of expansion of the universe (assuming the linear relation he had found on theoretical grounds);

3. that, at the time of publication, the limited popularity of the journal in which Lemaître's paper appeared and the language used made his remarkable discovery largely unperceived by the astronomical community;

4. that both Georges Lemaître (an IAU member since 1925) and the American astronomer Edwin Hubble (an IAU member since 1922) attended the 3rd IAU General Assembly in Leiden in July 1928 and exchanged views about the relevance of the redshift vs distance observational data of the extragalactic nebulae to the emerging evolutionary model of the universe;

5. that Edwin Hubble, in 1929 published the paper entitled "A Relation between Distance and Radial Velocity among Extra-Galactic Nebulae" in which he proposed and derived the linear distance-velocity relation for galaxies, ultimately including new velocity data in his 1931 paper with Humason. Soon after the publication of his papers, the cosmic expansion became universally known as the "Hubble law";

6. that, in 1931, by invitation of the journal *Monthly Notices of the Royal Astronomical Society*, G. Lemaître translated in English his original 1927 paper, deliberately omitting the section in which he derived the rate of expansion because he "did not find it advisable to reprint the [his] provisional discussion of radial velocities which is clearly of no actual interest, and also the geometrical note, which

could be replaced by a small bibliography of old and new papers on the subject"; desiring

7. to pay tribute to both Georges Lemaître and Edwin Hubble for their fundamental contributions to the development of modern cosmology;

8. to honor the intellectual integrity of Georges Lemaître that made him value more the progress of science than his own visibility;

9. to highlight the role of the IAU General Assemblies in fostering exchanges of views and international discussions;

10. to inform future scientific discourses with historical facts; resolves

11. to recommend that from now on the expansion of the universe be referred to as the "Hubble-Lemaître law."

The proposed resolution was accepted, with 78 percent of the votes in favor, 20 percent against, and 2 percent abstaining.

Beyond this praiseworthy initiative to honor Lemaître, it was not clear at the time whether the IAU's recommendation would be widely followed by specialized cosmology articles and in the popular science media, or whether laziness and habit would prevail.

A more meaningful and lasting tribute, suggested in recent years by a few historically informed scientists, would be to name one of the large space telescopes dedicated to cosmology after Lemaître. It would be rather naïve to propose the idea to NASA, the US space agency. Rather, it is the European Planck Telescope, launched in 2009, that would have better deserved the name of the Belgian physicist. In 2014, the fifth and last Automated Transfer Vehicle (ATV) designed by the European Space Agency to carry a few tons of cargo to the International Space Station (ISS), orbiting 400 km from Earth, was eventually named ATV5-Georges Lemaître. Launched by Ariane rocket in Kourou, French Guiana, on July 29, 2014, ATV-5 was moored to the International Space Station on August 12, 2014.

This is progress. However, even in Europe, Lemaître is not yet unanimously recognized as the real father of Big Bang cosmology.

10. The Quantum Birth

of the Universe (1931)

If you break the nucleus of the atom,
You will find there enclosed the Sun.
—Sayyed Ahmad Hastef Isfahanî, *Ode to Divine Unity*

T**HE YEAR 1931 CAN UNDOUBTEDLY BE CALLED** Georges Lemaître's
annus mirabilis.[1] Indeed, a series of major contributions to relativistic cosmology by the Belgian physicist and priest appeared in the
brief period of a few months:

1. "A Homogeneous Universe of Constant Mass and Increasing
    Radius Accounting for the Radial Velocity of Extra-Galactic
    Nebulae," in the March 7 issue of the *Monthly Notices of the
    Royal Astronomical Society*.[2] This was the English translation
    of the article published four years earlier in French, in which
    Lemaître was the first to interpret the astronomical data about
    the galaxy redshifts as a positively curved space model in which
    the universe slowly expanded from an equilibrium Einstein
    state at t = $-\infty$ (see Chapter 9).

2. "The Expanding Universe," in the same issue of the *MNRAS*.[3]
    Here Lemaître calculated that the expansion of space could be
    induced by a preceding phase of "stagnation" some 10^{10} years in
    the past.

3. A short note, "The Beginning of the World from the Point of View of Quantum Theory," published in the May 9 issue of *Nature*.

4. "Contribution to a Discussion about the Question of the Relation of the Physical Universe to Life and Mind," published in the October 24 issue of *Supplement to Nature*, in which Lemaître advocated an abrupt beginning of the universe from an initial, superdense concentration of nuclear matter called the "primeval atom."

5. "*L'expansion de l'espace*," a quantitative account of 3) and 4) published in French in the November 20 issue of *Revue des Questions Scientifiques*, a Belgian scientific journal.[4] Here the author developed his major cosmological ideas about the primeval atom hypothesis in an extraordinary literary style (see Chapter 13).

Additionally, Lemaître, fascinated by the brand-new theory of quantum mechanics, also published two papers on the subject that same year:

6. "*L'indétermination de la loi de Coulomb*," in the August 8 issue of the *Annales de la Société Scientifique de Bruxelles*, in which he applied Heisenberg's uncertainty principle to the Coulomb law.

7. "*Sur l'interprétation d'Eddington de l'équation de Dirac*," in the same issue, in which he investigated the mathematical structure of quantum electrodynamics by using the formalism of quaternions.

Near the middle of this string of pearls, the smallest (fewer than 500 words) but brightest contribution (#3) can be considered the true "charter" of the modern Big Bang theory.

Like many other physicists, Lemaître was quite impressed by the new quantum mechanics. Because of this interest, he had accepted an invitation from the British Association for Science in London to participate in its annual conference, devoted to the relationship between "the physical universe and the life of the mind." Lemaître there proposed the idea of a singular origin of the expanding universe and sketched the model of the primeval atom. As mentioned above, the singular creation of the universe had been briefly discussed by Friedmann, but totally ignored by the scientific community. Lemaître then published his remarkable letter in the May 9, 1931, issue of the journal *Nature*:

Sir Arthur Eddington states that, philosophically, the notion of a beginning of the present order of Nature is repugnant to him.[5] I would rather be inclined to think that the present state of quantum theory suggests a beginning of the world very different from the present order of Nature.

Thermodynamical principles from the point of view of quantum theory may be stated as follows:

(1) Energy of constant total amount is distributed in discrete quanta.

(2) The number of distinct quanta is ever increasing.

If we go back in the course of time we must find fewer and fewer quanta, until we find all the energy of the universe packed in a few or even in a unique quantum.

Now, in atomic processes, the notions of space and time are no more than statistical notions; they fade out when applied to individual phenomena involving a small number of quanta. If the world has begun with a single quantum, the notions of space and time would altogether fail to have any meaning at the beginning; they would only begin to have a sensible meaning when the original quantum had been divided into a sufficient number of quanta. If this suggestion is correct, the beginning of the world happened a little before the beginning of space and time. I think that such a beginning of the world is far enough from the present order of Nature to be not at all repugnant.

It may be difficult to follow up the idea in detail as we are not yet able to count the quantum packets in every case. For example, it may be that an atomic nucleus must be counted as a unique quantum, the atomic number acting as a kind of quantum number. If the future development of quantum theory happens to turn in that direction, we could conceive the beginning of the universe in the form of a unique atom, the atomic weight of which is the total mass of the universe.

This highly unstable atom would divide in smaller and smaller atoms by a kind of super-radioactive process. Some remnant of this process might, according to Sir James Jeans's idea, foster the heat of the stars until our low atomic number atoms allowed life to be possible.

Clearly the initial quantum could not contain in itself the whole course of evolution; but, according to the principle of indeterminacy, that is not necessary. Our world is now understood to be a world where something really happens; the whole story of the world need not have been written down in the first quantum like a song on the disc of a phonograph. The whole matter of the world must have been present at the beginning, but the story it has to tell may be written step by step.[6]

This extraordinary text was a scathing response to a speech made shortly before by Arthur Eddington to the Mathematical Association on January 5, 1931, and published in the March 21 issue of *Nature*.[7] The British astrophysicist initially paid tribute to Lemaître, declaring, "We have recently learnt, mainly through the work of Prof. Lemaître, that spherical space is expanding rather rapidly." Dealing with the role of entropy as an arrow in time, Eddington considered that, following time backwards, one would find more and more organization in the world, up to a state of minimum entropy. But, for philosophical reasons, Eddington refused to go back further in time to the concept of a singularity. Otherwise, "We have come to an abrupt end of space-time—only we generally call it the 'beginning.'"

If in 1931, Eddington and some other physicists, including Einstein, began to accept the new cosmological paradigm of a dynamical universe instead of a static one (both for theoretical and observational reasons), few of them were ready to accept one of the possible (but not necessary) consequences of that—namely that the expansion had begun a finite time in the past, starting from an absolute beginning. For them, this question lay outside the range of science, and thus in his speech Eddington added that "philosophically the notion of a beginning of the present order of Nature is repugnant to me."[8]

In response Lemaître argued that the world had come into existence a finite time ago in an explosive event, which he likened to a giant radioactive flash. Just like Eddington, he supposed that time and its arrow are connected to the growth of entropy. In the direction of increasing time, the universe evolves to a state of maximum entropy, i.e., of complete disorganization. In the direction of the past, the universe would have proceeded from a state of zero entropy. Eddington had wondered whether the moment of zero entropy could mark the beginning of the world. Lemaître disagreed and pointed out that entropy is a measurement of proper time, and not of the time-coordinate; consequently, Eddington was wrong to believe that the moment of minimal entropy separated "before creation" from "after creation" on an axis of universal time. It should be seen, on the contrary, like an essential singularity, where the concepts of space and time lose their meaning. In order for space-time to exist within the framework of general relativity, one needs a tensor of matter-energy, due to the identification of geometry with matter. The state of matter with zero entropy constitutes a singularity of the matter-energy tensor on the right-hand side of the field equations, which is equivalent to a singularity in the curvature tensor on the left-hand side. There was no time nor space prior to the state of condensation at zero entropy. It was the initial singularity that created space-time. Thus, the plurality and the diversity of the physical world appeared to come from "something" physical, coinciding with the $R=0$ singularity of relativistic cosmological models. The atom-universe exploded and plurality emerged. The entropy became non-zero, while time and its arrow also appeared.

The radical innovation introduced by Lemaître thus consisted of linking the structure of the universe at large scales with the intimate nature of the atoms—in other words, relating the early universe to quantum mechanics.[9] Lemaître used the term "unique quantum" and took care to stress that at this stage, the laws of physics as we know them had no meaning, because the concepts of space and time were not yet defined. As Lemaître conceived it, this is the frontier of science; and in the present-day quantum cosmology, nothing clearly indicates that this frontier of physical knowledge, called the Planck era and corresponding to a time of 10^{-43} seconds, can be crossed. Lemaître's idea corresponds well with what is now called quantum cosmology.

Let us analyze in more detail Lemaître's argument. He begins by stating that in the course of time, the number of distinct quanta is ever increasing. He would explain this assertion more clearly in a semi-popular paper published later in the same year (see the next chapter). Let two volumes V_1 and V_2 contain heat radiation at temperatures T_1 and T_2, and let T be the equilibrium temperature of the total volume V_1+V_2. From the law of energy conservation it follows that $V_1T_1^4 + V_2T_2^4 = (V_1+V_2)T^4$, and the number of photons will increase proportionally to $(V_1+V_2)T^3 - V_1T_1^3 - V_2T_2^3$, which is always positive. The demonstration is valid only for a gas of photons and not for material particles, but Lemaître generalizes it by assuming in an intuitive way that the number of particles sharing a given amount of energy is constantly increasing.

Next, Lemaître continues his short text by following closely an argument by Niels Bohr published a few months before.[10] According to this argument, the concepts of space and time in quantum mechanics have only statistical validity. As a consequence, when the number of quanta was reduced to a single quantum, as assumed to be the case at the beginning of the world, the notions of space and time failed. They received meaning only when the original quantum began to disintegrate. Therefore, the beginning of the world (namely the single quantum) happened "a little before" the beginning of space and time. The phrasing is equivocal, since "a little before" seems to imply a temporal sense, which would be contradictory to the idea that time did not yet exist. Lemaître wanted to say that space and time emerged from the original quantum in a logical sense.

Now, what did he consider the original quantum to be made of? Lemaître suggested that it might be a huge atomic nucleus, with an extremely large atomic number corresponding to the total mass of the universe and acting like a quantum number. In 1931, nuclear physics was still in its infancy and the neutron had not yet been discovered; but Lemaître knew about radioactive processes, and he hypothesized that a huge atom would be unstable and explosively decay into a large number of quanta. As he explained later, the word "atom" had to be taken in the Greek sense, as something completely undifferentiated and without physical properties.

In the final paragraph, Lemaître appealed to the Heisenberg uncertainty (or indeterminacy) principle to express the idea that the whole course of cosmic evolution was not written down in the first quantum.

Lemaître's note was not an ordinary scientific communication, but rather "a visionary piece of cosmo-poetry that was meant to open the eyes of the readers rather than convince them."[11] He wanted to make his own view concerning the beginning of the world publicly known and understood by everyone; thus, he did not introduce any equations. In addition, he chose to sign his communication as a private person, namely "G. Lemaître, 40 rue Namur, Louvain," and not as a distinguished physicist and cosmologist, professor at the University of Louvain.

The Priest and the Scientist

"Lemaître was a great scientist but he was also a Catholic priest with a deep faith," Dominique Lambert reminds us. Lambert continues:

> Since his ordination in 1923, he belonged to a sacerdotal fraternity founded by Cardinal Mercier called "Les Amis de Jésus" (The Friends of Jesus), in which priests pronounced some vows unusual for secular priests, for example the vow of poverty. He had good relations with his hierarchy. In 1935, he was made honorary Canon of Saint Rombaut Cathedral in Mechelen (Malines).
>
> One year later, Pius XI chose him in the first list of members of the Pontifical Academy of Sciences. Succeeding Fr. Agostino Gemelli, Lemaître was appointed by John XXIII as President of the Pontifical Academy of Sciences, in 1960, and on that occasion he was elevated to the rank of Domestic Prelate.[12]

Since the creation of the universe a finite time ago is a dogma in Christian thought, it might be tempting to conclude that Lemaître's model of an explosive universe was motivated by the aim to reconcile relativistic cosmology with religious belief. Here it is interesting to point out that the manuscript (typed) version of Lemaître's 1931 article in *Nature*, preserved in the Archives Lemaître at the University of Louvain, ended with a sentence crossed out by Lemaître himself and which, therefore, was never published. Lemaître initially intended to conclude his letter to *Nature* with this: "I think that every one who believes in a supreme being supporting every being and every act, believes also that God is essentially hidden and may be glad to see how present physics provides a veil hiding the creation."

the universe in the form of a unique atom whose atomic weight is the total mass of the universe. This highly unstable atom would divide in smaller and smaller atoms by a kind of super-radioactive process. Some rest of this process would, according to Sir Jeans idea, foster the heat of the stars until our low atomic number atoms may allow live to be possible.

Clearly the initial quantum could not conceile in itself the whole course of evolution; but, according to the indetermination principle, that is not necessary. Our world is now a world where something happens; the whole story of the world does not need to be written down in the first quantum as a song on the disc of a phonograp. The whole matter of the world must be present at the beginning, but the story it has to tell may be written step by step.

I think that every one who believes in a supreme being supporting avery being and every acting, believes also that God is essentially hidden and may be glad to see how present physics provides a veil hiding the creation.

Figure 10.1.
Manuscript version of Lemaître's 1931 article for *Nature*, with an interesting sentence crossed out by Lemaître himself.

The deleted sentence reflects his view that God is hidden, not to be found as the Creator at the beginning of the universe. But before sending his paper to *Nature*, Lemaître may have decided that such a reference to God would make his scientific paper feel more rather than less theological in orientation. Or he may have realized that whereas this was his view of God, it was by no means a universally accepted theological position in the Judeo-Christian tradition, as the deleted sentence seemed to assert. In either case, it was a can of worms he decided not to open.

According to the analysis of the most qualified specialist on the subject, Dominique Lambert,[13] Lemaître preserved all his life the conception of a supreme and inaccessible God of whom the prophet Isaiah speaks, enabling him to keep the natural origin of the world within the strict limits of physics, without mixing it with a super-natural creation. As a priest, and as a theologian, Lemaître was very conscious of the potential conflict—or, perhaps, the possibility of concordance—between the Christian dogma of a world created by God and the scientific theory of a universe formed approximately ten billion years ago.

In his youth, however, Lemaître was briefly tempted to unify science and religion. During the First World War (which began just after he got his bachelor's degree in engineering sciences), while fighting in important battles, Lemaître dedicated time for prayer and for reading science books, such as *Electricité et Optique* by Poincaré. In parallel he meditated on the book of Genesis and the Psalms, and read carefully some books by Léon Bloy (1846–1917), a famous Catholic writer who was a close friend of the Christian poet Charles Péguy and of the neo-Thomistic philosopher Jacques Maritain. Lemaître was then interested in building a unified religious and scientific synthesis. In the trenches he wrote a short essay entitled *"Les trois premières paroles de Dieu"* ("The Three First Words of God"), an attempt to give a kind of exegesis of the book of Genesis's first three verses in a concordist-like style. He sent this essay to Léon Bloy and met him, in Bourg-la-Reine, near Paris, during his furlough. Bloy, who died shortly afterwards, advised him to avoid any form of concordism, namely the attempt to mix on the same level scientific and theological subjects. Initially Lemaître was a little puzzled, but he followed this advice; afterwards, during all the rest of his sacerdotal and academic life, he would adopt just such a position.

In contrast to some other leading cosmologists who highlight scientific evidence that seems to point strongly to God,[14] Lemaître avoided using one of these two "ways of knowledge" to support the other. He took, for example, great care to distinguish between the "beginning" and the "creation" of the world, and never spoke about the initial state of the universe in terms of "creation" (unlike Friedmann, a fervent Orthodox Christian, who appears more "concordist" than the Belgian priest).

Lemaître held that science and theology dealt with two separate realms, and that the scientific cosmology of the Big Bang neither confirmed nor refuted the Christian notion of God's creation.

Lemaître's belief in two separate levels of understanding, one scientific and the other religious, did not imply, however, that he found cosmology irrelevant to religious thought. Yes, he believed that theological assumptions should not interfere with the scientist's scrupulous pursuit of the truth about the natural world. But he also was convinced that, on a broader ethical level, religious and philosophical values are important, even essential, to the scientist. With the humor he often displayed, he wrote in 1934 that searching for truth implies a search for the soul as well as for "spectra" (those of extragalactic nebulae).

In an interview given in 1933 upon his return to the United States, and reproduced in a long article in the *New York Times*, Lemaître clearly stated his conception of the relationship between science and religion:

> There is no conflict between science and religion…. Here we have this wonderful, this incessantly interesting and exciting universe. When we try to learn more about it, learn how it began and how it is put together, to find what it is all about, as you say in America, what are we doing? Only seeking the truth. And is not truth-seeking a service to God? Certainly everything in the Bible and in all authoritative Christian doctrine teaches that it is. Has any logical religious thinker of any faith ever denied it?…
> Once you realize that the Bible does not purport to be a textbook of science, the old controversy between religion and science vanishes….

There is no reason to abandon the Bible because we now believe that it took perhaps ten thousand million years to create what we think is the universe. Genesis is simply trying to teach us that one day in seven should be devoted to rest, worship, and reverence—all necessary to salvation....

As a matter of fact, neither St. Paul nor Moses had the slightest idea of relativity. The writers of the Bible were illuminated more or less—some more than others—by the question of salvation. On other questions they were as wise or as ignorant as their generation. Hence it is utterly unimportant that errors of historic and scientific fact should be found in the Bible, especially if errors relate to events that were not directly observed by those who wrote about them. The idea that because they were right in their doctrine of immortality and salvation they must also be right on all other subjects is simply the fallacy of people who have an incomplete understanding of why the Bible was given to us at all....

When men were told that they had the right to interpret the Bible's teachings according to their own lights... naturally some were bound to decide that its science was infallible and others that it did not agree with modern instrumental measurements and was proof of opposite doctrines. The conflict has always been between those who fail to understand the true scope of either science or religion. For those who understand both, the conflict is simply about descriptions of what goes on in other people's minds.[15]

Lemaître would also express this more "officially" in his speech at the 1958 Solvay Conference, where he mentioned that the Big Bang theory remained totally outside of any metaphysical or religious question.

In the meantime, an important episode happened, namely the famous 1951 address *Un'ora* ("The Proofs of the Existence of God in the Light of Modern Natural Sciences"), given by Pope Pius XII before the Pontifical Academy of Sciences, which implicitly referred to the primeval atom hypothesis but without quoting Lemaître explicitly:

Contemporary science, with one sweep back across the centuries, has succeeded in bearing witness to the august instant of the primordial *Fiat Lux,* which along with the matter there burst forth from nothing a sea of light and radiation.... Thus, with that concreteness which is characteristic of physical proofs, modern science has confirmed the contingency of the universe and also the well-founded deduction of the epoch when the world came forth from the hands of the creator.

As well explained by Dominique Lambert, whose analysis I follow very closely in the rest of this chapter,[16] the pontifical talk is often read as a defense of the primeval atom hypothesis with a concordist-like style. The pope did see Lemaître's discovery as friendly to theistic belief but was considerably more nuanced and measured than many a concordist in making his case. The address sought to show that the proofs of God's existence formulated by St. Thomas Aquinas can be revitalized with new supports in contemporary science. The *Un'ora* address suggests that physics (thermodynamics, nuclear physics, cosmology) can bring some data to defend the mutability of the universe and then to give a new foundation to initiate the Thomistic proof of the existence of God based on motion, i.e., change. This was explicitly noted by Thomistic philosopher Fernand Van Steenberghen of the University of Louvain—a colleague of Lemaître, who like him was a member of "Les Amis de Jésus." In his book entitled *Dieu Caché: Comment Savons-Nous Que Dieu Existe?* (*Hidden God: How Do We Know that God Exists?*), he wrote, referring to the address *Un'ora*:

> Pius XII was deeply struck and obviously delighted by the recent discoveries of physics and by the new orientation they give to the cosmogonic theories of scientists. Far from contradicting the theses of traditional philosophy or the data of Christian revelation, physics reveals facts which reinforce the empirical starting points of the philosophical proofs of the existence of God.... However, as one may have noticed, each time his admiration for the discoveries of science risks leading him to imprudent declarations, Pius XII stops in time and brings the necessary nuances and reservations: on their own, he says, the sciences cannot prove the existence of God; it is when he thinks as a philosopher that the scientist succeeds.[17]

Nevertheless, Lemaître worried that the pope's address could suggest to many astronomers that his cosmological hypothesis of the primeval atom had been conceived for apologetic reasons. Lemaître wished to emphasize that his theories were not driven by apologetics but by data and the search for scientific truth. Furthermore, he knew better than anyone that the hypothesis was not yet confirmed by observations. In 1952, stopping at the Vatican on a trip to South Africa, he succeeded in advising the pope, who had to deliver a speech to the Eighth General Assembly of the International Astronomical Union, not to refer to the primeval atom. For this Lemaître consulted with two men, Father O'Connell, who was a science advisor to Pius XII, and the Cardinal Secretary of State. Lemaître's short visit had the intended effect. The new pope's speech primarily praised the advances in astrophysics research in the last fifty years, making only a brief statement on the Big Bang, namely that "the human spirit, upon considering the vast paths traveled by galaxies, becomes in some manner a spectator at the cosmic events that occurred on the very morning of creation."[18]

And Pius XII never mentioned the primeval atom hypothesis again. In a conference in 1963 entitled "Univers et Atome," Lemaître declared, concerning the papal address: "It is clear that the attitude of the Pontiff is on his own ground and has no relation to Eddington's or my theories. Moreover, my name is not mentioned in the Pope's speech."

For Lemaître, creation was not a question of beginning. In a text published long after his death but written at the end of the 1930s, he said:

What happened before that? Before that we have to face the zero value of the radius (of the universe). We have discussed how far it had to be taken as strictly zero, and we have seen that it means a very trifling quantity, let us say a few light-hours. We may speak of this as a beginning; I do not say a creation. Physically it is a beginning in the sense that if something had happened before it, it has no observable influence on the behavior of our universe, as any feature of matter before this beginning has been completely lost by the extreme contraction at the theoretical zero. A pre-existence of the universe has a metaphysical character. Physically, everything happens as if the theoretical zero was really a beginning. The question whether it was really a beginning or rather a creation, something starting from nothing, is a philosophical question that cannot be settled by physical or astronomical considerations.[19]

In a beautiful memorial article on Lemaître, written for the Pontifical Academy of Sciences in 1968, Paul Dirac recalls that one day they were chatting about cosmic evolution and that, feeling stimulated by the grandeur of the image that the Belgian scholar-priest had given, Dirac told him that he thought cosmology was the branch of science that was closest to religion. But Lemaître did not agree with Dirac. After careful consideration, he suggested instead that the scientific discipline closest to religion was psychology.

11. The Expansion
of Space (1931)

For sure, until now I hadn't seen,
not really seen the sky.
—Henri Michaux, "Le dépouillement par l'espace" (1966)

G EORGES LEMAÎTRE HAD TO CONVINCE OTHERS THAT THE CRUCIAL
idea of the birth of the universe from a "primeval atom" was
physically realistic. He thus prepared a quantitative article to be published in the fall of 1931. In the interval, he accepted the invitation of
the British Association for Science to take part in its centenary meeting, to be held in London on September 29, including a session on
cosmology devoted to "The Question of the Relation of the Physical
Universe to Life and Mind." James Jeans, Arthur Eddington, Arthur
Milne, Willem de Sitter, and Robert Millikan also made scientific
contributions.[1] Among other questions, they had to deal with the
problem of the age of the universe, which, when deduced from the
Hubble constant known at the time, gave a value of about 1.8 billion
years, conspicuously shorter than the time required for stellar evolution, as emphasized by Jeans and others.

Lemaître argued (without any explicit calculation) that the problem could be solved by making use of the stagnation process he had
previously introduced in the context of the Eddington-Lemaître
model.[2] But he went much further by putting forward his suggestion
of an abrupt beginning of the universe. As he said, "A complete revision of our cosmological hypothesis is necessary, the primary condition

being the test of rapidity. We want a 'fireworks' theory of evolution... It is quite possible to have a variation of the radius of the universe going on, expanding from zero to the actual value."[3]

The singular creation of the universe had been briefly hypothesized by Friedmann, but completely ignored by the scientific community. Lemaître refined the argument and introduced for the first time (as far as I know) the expression *primeval atom*:

> I would picture the evolution as follows: at the origin, all the mass of the universe would exist in the form of a unique atom; the radius of the universe, although not strictly zero, being relatively very small. The whole universe would be produced by the disintegration of this primeval atom. It can be shown that the radius of space must increase.... Whether this is wild imagination or physical hypothesis cannot be said at present, but we may hope that the question will not wait too long to be solved.[4]

Lemaître also suggested that the cosmic rays, which had been recently discovered, were the fossils of the original explosion, as "ashes and smoke of bright but very rapid fireworks.... We are thus led to the conclusion that the stars were born some ten thousand million years ago without atmospheres, and that the cosmic rays are outstanding features of the formation of a star."[5]

Lemaître quantitatively developed the model of the primeval atom in "L'Expansion de l'Espace," published in French in the *Revue des Questions Scientifiques* of November 1931. He assumed a positively curved space (with elliptic topology), time-varying matter density and pressure, and a cosmological constant such that, starting from a singularity, the universe first expanded, then passed through a phase of "stagnation" during which its radius coasted to that of Einstein's static solution, then started again an accelerated expansion.

Lemaître's approach differs starkly from Friedmann's, as much in the scientific argument itself as in its form. Regarding the argument, Friedmann's approach was axiomatic; Lemaître's, physical. As for the form, Lemaître's is very literary, adapted to the public conferences Lemaître frequently participated in. The style is a model of rigor mixed with lyricism, readable by almost anyone, and testifying to the years of study Lemaître devoted to Greek and Latin. As André Deprit has pointed out, in 1908–1909 the young Lemaître had taken a poetry class under the direction of Franz Charlier, who had earned a reputation as a ruthless critic of style.[6]

Annotating Lemaître

Here I shall present extracts of Lemaître's extraordinary 1946 book, *L'Hypothèse de l'atome primitif* (*The Primeval Atom*),[7] omitting technical developments and appending notes to clarify Lemaître's argument.

Lemaître writes:

> Following the Laplace and Kant cosmogonies, we became accustomed to taking a very diffuse nebula as the starting point for evolution, a nebula filling all space and becoming more and more condensed by splitting into partial nebulae and finally into stars.[8]

The French astronomer and mathematician Pierre-Simon Laplace (1749–1827) suggested the hypothesis of the primitive nebula in Chapter 6 of his *System of the World* (1824 edition). According to him, the solar system originated in a vast, flattened, slowly rotating cloud of gas that contracted and cooled. Current models of solar system formation differ little from this prototype.

The German philosopher Immanuel Kant (1724–1804) published his cosmological conceptions in *Naturgeschichte des Himmels* (1755).[9] Kant presents the nebular hypothesis on the formation of the solar system, proposes that the Milky Way is a large cluster of stars of flattened form, and suggests that there are many other "island universes" of the same type.

Lemaître writes:

> This very old idea has been adapted to the recent progress of astronomy. It has been recently expanded in that fine book which Sir James Jeans dedicated to the study of the universe.[10]

James Hopwood Jeans (1877–1946), an English astronomer, wanted to show that Laplace's hypothesis on the formation of the solar system was incorrect. He proposed a theory of his own, in which tidal forces triggered by the passage of a star in the vicinity of the sun would have torn matter from it, which would then have condensed into planets. (This theory has since been abandoned.) Jeans was a prolific author of popular books such as *Astronomy and Cosmogony* (1928), *The Universe Around Us* (1929), *The Mysterious Universe* (1930), and *Through Space and Time* (1934), all published by Cambridge University Press.

Lemaître continues:

> We are now in a position to estimate the density of the primeval nebula by evaluating the mass and the distances of smaller condensations of stars, called the extra-galactic nebulae, which enclose all that we know of the universe. If the actual mass of the stars was supposed to be distributed uniformly throughout the whole space that they occupy, one would find that the primeval nebula must have been more rarefied than the highest vacuum which our physicists can hope to achieve in their laboratories. The density of the universe reduces to 10^{-31} grams per cubic centimeter, a figure which is generally considered to be reliable within a factor of one hundred.[11]

As previously mentioned, Edwin Hubble had demonstrated the extragalactic nature of spiral nebulae in 1925.[12] The value indicated by Lemaître is significantly lower than what was commonly accepted in his time, which was about 10^{-26} g/cm³. For instance, Einstein, in his Rhodes Lectures of 1931, declared that "the average density is represented by a fraction whose numerator is 1, and whose denominator is 1 followed by 26 or 27 zeros."[13] But nearly a century later, with the benefit of much more advanced astronomical instruments, astronomers have settled on an estimated density of 5×10^{-30} g/cm³, an estimate much closer to Lemaître's estimate. Here again, Lemaître shows exceptional intuition.

Next, Lemaître tackles a difficulty confronting his theory:

> The idea of a primeval nebula has to meet a very serious difficulty which can be removed only with the help of the theory of relativity

and of non-euclidean geometries: the different parts of the nebula are pulled together by gravity, and it seems as though they should have to collapse toward their center of gravity. A first element of a solution is brought about by the possibility that real space is not euclidean but should obey the laws of Riemann's elliptic geometry. Then there is no longer a center of gravity.[14]

He continues shortly thereafter:

All points of the nebula remain uniformly distributed in space; the distance between any two of them is always the same fraction of the total length of the closed straight line on which they lie; but this length, equal to πR, varies with the radius R; every distance varies in the same ratio as the variation of the radius of space.

To study in detail the variation of the radius of space, it is necessary to appeal to the equations of general relativity. It is possible, however, to illustrate the result of relativistic computation by elementary considerations involving the laws of classical mechanics.[15] This is possible because the laws of relativity are reduced as a limit to the laws of Newton, when they are applied to an infinitely small volume.[16]

And then:

These equations account for the dynamics of the universe; they accustom us to thinking of the radius of the universe as a physical quantity, able to vary. The manner in which these equations have been obtained must not be regarded as rigorous demonstration. A demonstration which is not open to criticism can be deduced only from the general equations of relativity.[17]

For Lemaître, the Newtonian derivation of the laws of cosmic dynamics is only a pedagogical convenience, and in no way reflects the true (relativistic) nature of the problem. After the publication of Milne and McCrea's paper in 1934, several cosmologists would try to prove that the Newtonian approach is equivalent to the relativistic approach—which would cast doubt on the very usefulness of general relativity in cosmology.[18]

Lemaître writes:

Nevertheless, the elementary considerations evolved hitherto may allow us, in some degree, to grasp the physical significance of results involving more abstract methods. Now we must explain what change must be made in these equations, in order to account for the equilibrium of the Laplace nebula, and to show how this change can be justified.

One of the most important achievements of the theory of relativity is the identification of the idea of mass with that of energy. Energy is essentially a quantity which is defined, except for an additive constant; mass, on the contrary, insofar as it affects the law of universal gravity, does not involve any arbitrary constant.

The identification of mass with energy, therefore, admits of a choice of the constant of energy, or, inversely, of the introduction of an arbitrary constant to the expression of the gravitational mass.[19]

This point, relating to the need for a cosmological constant, would later be the subject of a controversy between Lemaître and Einstein. (See Appendix 3 for the letter from Lemaître to Einstein, dated July 30, 1947, followed by the latter's reply on September 26.)

Lemaître continues:

The theory of relativity teaches us the manner in which this arbitrary constant must be introduced. The equations of gravity are obtained by integration of equations which express both the conservation of energy and momentum. This integration naturally introduces a constant of integration. But this constant of integration is not added to the energy or to the total mass; it is added to the density. In other words, the necessary adjustment between energy and gravitational mass is made, not on the total mass, but on the density. This arbitrary constant, which is introduced in the equations, has been called the "cosmological constant" because it has no importance except in problems involving the whole universe.[20]

Let us recall that Einstein introduced this constant in his 1917 article "Kosmologische Betrachtungen zur allgemeinen Relativitätstheorie," to ensure the static character of his cosmological model.[21]

Lemaître writes:

The interpretation of the cosmological term is straightforward. It means that an elastic force, which tends to augment the radius, is superposed on the Newtonian force, which tends to diminish it. A value of the radius exists, called the equilibrium radius, for which these two forces neutralize one another. The nebula of Laplace will last, provided that the value of the radius be suitably adjusted to the value of the total mass of the nebula.

Thus we have succeeded in making the Laplace nebula maintain equilibrium. Let us not rejoice too soon, because we shall have to realize that this equilibrium is quite precarious.[22]

In other words, Einstein's model of the static universe is unstable at the slightest disturbance. The instability was already apparent, in Newtonian theory, in the equilibrium of a self-gravitating static mass.

We can therefore conclude that the formation of local condensations in the Laplace nebula in equilibrium must have upset this equilibrium and initiated the universe.

This is the second expansion which, in Lemaître's model of the "hesitating universe" (See Figure 11.1.), is triggered at the end of the era of stagnation and inaugurates the present era of accelerated expansion.

The hypothesis of Laplace has, therefore, as its consequence, the expansion of space. Does this expansion actually take place, and with what speed is it produced?

In a space with increasing radius, the material points, the great extra-galactic nebulae, for example, remain uniformly distributed in space. Nevertheless, their mutual distances increase, all in the same ratio. Thus, if we observe the extra-galactic nebulae, we shall be able to state that their distances increase while remaining proportional to one other and therefore that all extra-galactic nebulae have velocities of recession proportional to their distance. The velocities of stars or of nebulae are observed through the displacement of their spectral lines, known by the name of the Doppler-Fizeau effect.[23]

Christian Doppler (1803–1853) and Armand Fizeau (1819–1896) discovered the law of frequency (or wavelength) shift of a source as a function of the relative speed between the source and the observer.

> The spectrum of distant nebulae shows displacement towards the red, corresponding to velocities of recession up to 10,000 kilometers per second; and insofar as it is possible to judge their distances, these velocities are quite proportional to this distance. Up to now, we possess about a hundred measurements of velocity, and, as a consequence of all these measurements, we can estimate that a nebula located at a distance of one hundred million light years (a distance at which it is still possible to photograph the nebula) has a velocity of recession equal to one-twentieth of the speed of light, that is, about 15,000 kilometers per second.[24]

Recall from Chapter 9 that in 1912 Vesto Slipher, at the Lowell Observatory, discovered a systematic redshift, except for the closest galaxies.

That velocities are proportional is the law already presented by Lemaître in his 1927 article, and presented again by Hubble in 1929. For his 1929 article, Hubble had forty-six radial gears. Only four of them were negative—for the Andromeda galaxy (M31), its two companion galaxies, M32 and NGC 205, and the Triangle galaxy (M33)—while all the others were positive.

The coefficient of proportionality between distance and distance speed is the "Hubble constant." The value given by Lemaître, 15,000 kilometers per second per one hundred million light-years, is the value provided by Hubble in 1929, i.e., 500 kilometers per second per megaparsec (the megaparsec being equal to 3.26 million light-years). This value later turned out to be too high: Hubble had in fact underestimated the absolute magnitudes of the brightest stars, called Cepheids. Hubble's "constant" decreased by a factor of 10 between 1930 and 1965, following Walter Baade's work on Cepheids.[25] Today it is thought that the value is certainly between 50 and 100 km/s Mpc, and the different measurement methods converge towards 70 km/s Mpc.

Lemaître, referring to his estimate of the coefficient of proportionality, notes that "this result permits us to estimate the size which the nebula of Laplace would have had originally, and it determines the initial radius of equilibrium of space at about one billion light years."[26]

In his cosmological model, Lemaître adjusts the value of the cosmological constant so that the universe, after a period of rapid expansion, goes through a quasi-static (i.e., constant radius) phase similar to Einstein's static model. For this reason, his model is sometimes called the "hesitating universe." What he calls "initial equilibrium radius" of the nebula is thus the radius of this phase of "stagnation," equal to the radius of Einstein's universe R_E. It is during this phase that he thinks that galaxies were formed by condensation. This formation of galaxies would in turn have generated instability that would have triggered the expansion movement again, the universe entering the Hubble period. Lemaître writes:

> The present value of the radius depends on the estimate of the density of matter. In utilizing the value which we indicated at the beginning of this section, we find that it is equal to a dozen times the initial radius. The present state of the expansion enables us to get some idea, not only of the primeval nebula, but also of the epoch in which the local condensations were formed while initiating the expansion of space.[27]

That is twenty billion light years for the radius of the observable universe. The current estimate is forty-five billion light years, a higher value due to the fact that the age of the universe has been revised upwards.

Lemaître continues:

> If the world began as a Laplace nebula in equilibrium, the first general condensation of any importance which took place in it, and which therefore initiated the expansion of space, could not have occurred at an epoch dating back more than one hundred billion years.
>
> To realize the importance of this result, one must not forget that the cosmogony of Laplace-Jeans is a slow cosmogony. The

primeval gaseous masses are condensed as a result of small inequalities in their initial distribution and form the first condensations: the extra-galactic nebulae. As we have just seen, this event dates back only one hundred billion years, at a maximum. These nebulae were still gaseous at that time. Weak condensations then formed, by chance, and, as Jeans has shown, they must tend to increase provided that they be of sufficient dimension, comparable to the mutual distances of the stars. But how much time is necessary for these vast condensations to have the opportunity to be formed and to be able to be concentrated in a sphere whose diameter is a hundred thousand times smaller than their initial diameter?[28]

In current cosmological models, space became transparent after about 400,000 years of expansion. This period, known as the decoupling of matter and radiation, saw the emission of a blackbody radiation whose fossil glow can be observed today in the microwave domain. Lemaître writes:

Jeans asks one hundred thousand billion years for this evolution, and I am not sure that he has proved that this is enough; we can only give him one thousandth of this time. One hundred billion years is, at the most, fifty times the age attributed to the earth.[29]

The age attributed to the Earth today is 4.56 billion years, twice what it was thought to be in 1931.

Lemaître adds that one hundred billion years is also

one hundred times the amount of time necessary for the lunar tides to brake the rotation of our satellite and force it to turn the same face constantly towards the Earth. It is only a thousand times the amount of time which it takes light to come to us from nebula which have been photographed by our telescopes.[30]

The telescopes of the time were able to detect galaxies located about a hundred million light years away. Today we can detect galaxies close to the cosmological horizon, corresponding to a look-back time of thirteen billion years.

Next Lemaître asks:

Did evolution really take place according to Laplace's theory, starting with extreme diffuseness and reaching the present state of
matter: stellar condensations dispersed in a virtual vacuum? Light
would not require one minute to cross the Sun, and it would need
four years to reach the nearest star. The stellar world, like the atomic
world, seems to be extraordinarily empty. Even in a solid, there is
not one millionth of one millionth of the volume which is occupied
by atomic nuclei or electrons. A really complete cosmogony should
explain atoms as suns, and certainly atoms cannot have extreme
diffuseness as their origin.[31]

Ernest Rutherford (1871–1937) and Niels Bohr (1885–1962) were
the first to propose a "planetary model" of the atom, in which the mass
of the atom is concentrated in a small positively charged nucleus, while
the electrons occupy orbits located at the periphery of the atom. Their
model, largely in place by 1913, was unstable and, following the works
of Louis de Broglie and Erwin Schrödinger, would be replaced in the
1930s by the quantum model. Lemaître's emphasis on explaining "atoms as suns" shows his willingness to use atomic physics to elaborate
a complete cosmogonic scheme. However, although Lemaître had the
brilliant intuition that quantum mechanics should play a role in the
very beginning of the universe, he was not an expert in the field and
did not follow the latest advances in atomic physics (see Chapter 16).

Lemaître continues:

In the atomic field, we know about a spontaneous transformation
which can give us some idea of the direction of natural evolution; it
is the transformation of radioactive bodies.[32] Disregarding photons
and electrons, whose mass is nil or very small, an atom of uranium
is ultimately transformed into an atom of lead and eight atoms of
helium. This is a transformation from a state of greater condensation to one of lesser condensation. On the average, uranium can
remain extant for only four or five billion years before making its
transformation. Thorium behaves in an analogous way.[33]

Rutherford and Frederick Soddy had discovered that uranium and thorium transmuted into other elements by radioactive processes. The isotope 238 of uranium disintegrates in a characteristic time—called "half-life"—of 4.51 billion years, while the isotope 232 of thorium disintegrates in 14.1 billion years. The time scales being "cosmological," these two elements are used to date the oldest stars.

> If we had appeared on Earth one hundred billion years later, there would have been no appreciable amounts of radioactive substances, and we would doubtless have ended our tables of elements at bismuth and lead. Does the table of elements really end with uranium? Have we not come too late to know heavier elements which had almost completely disintegrated before our birth? Are not radioactive transformations a faint residue of the original evolution of the world and did they not take place, on the stellar scale, several billion years ago?[34]

The answer is *yes* regarding the naturally occurring elements. However, more massive elements can be synthesized in the laboratory. Uranium is element 92 of the periodic table. Neptunium, element 93, was synthesized in 1940, and in the 2016 update, the periodic table extends to element 118.

Most poetically, Lemaître writes:

> Our universe bears the marks of its youth and we can hope to reconstruct its story. The documents at our disposal are not buried in the piles of bricks carved by the Babylonians; our library does not risk being destroyed by fire; it is in space, admirably empty, where light waves are preserved better than sound is conserved on the wax of phonograph discs. The telescope is an instrument which looks far into space, but it is above all an instrument which looks far into the past. The light of nebulae tells us the history of a hundred million years ago, and all the events in the evolution of the world are at our disposal, written on fast waves in internebular ether.[35]

Lemaître then enters the section titled "The Primeval Atom":

> The world has proceeded from the condensed to the diffuse. The increase in entropy which characterizes the direction of evolution

is the progressive fragmentation of the energy which existed at the origin in a single unit. The atom-world was broken into fragments, each fragment into still smaller pieces. To simplify the matter, supposing that this fragmentation occurred in equal pieces, two hundred sixty generations would have been needed to reach the pulverization of matter into our poor little atoms, almost too small to be broken again.

The evolution of the world can be compared to a display of fireworks that has just ended: some few red wisps, ashes, and smoke. Standing on a well-chilled cinder, we see the slow fading of the suns, and we try to recall the vanished brilliance of the origin of the worlds.

The sun-atom splinters into fragments held together by universal attraction, fragments which splinter in their turn, hurling into the vacuum particles which are fast enough to escape the attraction of the entirety, sparks escaping from the burning crucible where the atom became a star. Rays travel in a straight line in the still-increasing desert of space, until they encounter a lost oasis, our galaxy, a chilled seed, our Earth, and discharge an electrometer, proving the formation of the suns.[36]

And then he poses the question:

Primeval nebula or primeval atom? Slow cosmogony or fast cosmogony? Gaseous cosmogony or radioactive cosmogony? How far must the old ideas be preserved? Was the Earth ejected in the atomic state by the sun-atom or was it separated from it in the gaseous phase? What are the properties of giant atoms and the laws which govern their disintegration? It would be premature to try to answer these questions.

In concluding, we must indicate the manner in which the theory of the expansion of the universe is adapted to the idea of the primeval atom. We can conceive of space beginning with the primeval atom and the beginning of space being marked by the beginning of time. The radius of space began at zero; the first stages of the expansion consisted of a rapid expansion determined by the mass of the initial atom, almost equal to the present mass of the universe. If this mass is sufficient, and the estimates which we can make indicate that it is indeed so, the initial expansion was able to permit the radius to exceed the value of the equilibrium radius. The expansion thus took place in three phases: a first period of rapid expansion in which the atom-universe was broken into atom-stars, a period of slowing-up, followed by a third period of accelerated expansion.[37] It is doubtless in the third period that we find ourselves today, and the acceleration of space which has followed the period of slowed expansion could well be responsible for the separation of stars into extra-galactic nebulae.[38]

This acceleration of cosmic expansion was experimentally demonstrated in 1998 by several teams, thanks to the observation of distant type Ia supernovas. For this, S. Perlmutter, B. Schmidt, and A. Riess won the 2011 Nobel Prize in Physics.

Lemaître, writing well before any such proof, continues:

It is not completely proven that we are not in the first period of expansion, and in this case, that the present expansion might not be capable of making us exceed the equilibrium radius, which would therefore be quite large. After having continued their movement of expansion for several billion years, the nebulae would stop, then fall back toward one other, and finally collide with one another, putting an end to the history of the world, with final fireworks, after which the radius of space would again be reduced to zero.

This hypothesis was proposed by Friedmann in 1922, and revived recently by Einstein. Against it, there are the present estimates of density, but these are not quite certain. Moreover, we can reassure ourselves by stating that space is still extending and that, even if the world must finish in this manner, we are living in a period that is closer to the beginning than to the end of the world.

But it is quite possible that the expansion has already passed the equilibrium radius, and will not be followed by a contraction. In this case, we need not expect anything sensational; the suns will become colder, the nebulae will recede, the cinders and smoke of the original fireworks will cool off and disperse.[39]

The picture of the end of the world within the framework of the Big Bang theory has hardly changed since Georges Lemaître. The very long-term fate of a universe in perpetual expansion has been limned by Frank Dyson and others.[40]

Science and Style

As can be seen, both the style and the scientific content of Lemaître's *The Primeval Atom* are of an amazing richness. Lemaître built his model from experimental data: the observation of the redshifts of remote nebulae, which he argued resulted from the expansion of space. At the same time, the very existence of these nebulae implied that, in its past, the universe underwent local processes of condensation which gave birth to these nebulae. For Lemaître, the expansion of space and the condensation of matter were the demonstrations of imbalances between two opposite cosmic forces: gravity (attractive) and the cosmological constant (repulsive).

Additionally, the observational results constrained the evolution of the world to a limited duration and implied a faster cosmogony than some had previously supposed. According to Hubble's calculated expansion rate of 540 km/s/Mpc and without a cosmological constant, the present universe should be about two billion years old. However, it was already known, by the study of radioactive elements, that the Earth was at least four billion years old. Obviously, the Earth could not be older than the universe. Lemaître thus doubly needed the cosmological constant, both to get an age of the universe compatible with that of the Earth, and to leave enough time for galactic condensations to form.

As illustrated in Figure 11.1, Lemaître's model divided the evolution of the universe into three distinct phases: two fast expansion phases separated by a period of deceleration. The first phase was an expansion of the explosive type, resulting from the radioactive decay of an atom-universe. The initial expansion was determined by the mass of the primeval atom, "almost equal to the present mass of the universe."[41] The word "almost" presumably referred to his early picture of the primeval atom as a huge condensation of nuclei. It was known from nuclear physics that an atomic nucleus is lighter than the sum of its constituent particles by an amount known as the mass defect.

Likewise, the primeval atom would be somewhat lighter than the galaxies resulting from its explosion. For this phase, Lemaître used the image of "fireworks" which, if poetic, is no less pedagogically debatable: it caused constant misunderstanding—repeated by popular accounts—presenting the beginning of the universe like an explosion of matter localized in outer space.

The second phase of Lemaître's model corresponded to a quasi-equilibrium between the density of matter and the cosmological constant, resulting in a practically constant radius during a period of stagnation. The attractive effects of gravitation being dominant at small scales, it was during this phase that the density fluctuations were formed, which eventually condensed to give rise to the large-scale structures of the universe, with stars grouped into galaxies and galaxies into clusters. The formation of local condensations disturbed the equilibrium conditions, which made the cosmological constant predominate and restarted the process of expansion. Thus, according to Lemaître, the universe is presently in the third stage.

Technically, the solution was obtained starting from the relativistic equations by supposing space with positive curvature and a cosmological constant λ slightly higher than the Einsteinian value $\lambda_E = 1/R_E^2$, where R_E was the equilibrium radius of Einstein's 1917 model of the universe. As to the age of the universe, Lemaître mentioned as a possible value ten billion years, but in his view it could be considerably higher, as it depended on the value of the cosmological constant. The duration of the stagnation phase depended essentially on $\lambda = \lambda_E(1+\varepsilon)$, being arbitrarily large when ε tended to zero.

In this sequence of three phases, the most arresting is the first, because it raises the question of the singular origin of the universe, which Lemaître dubbed the *primeval atom*. Here again, the terminology is colorful but scientifically debatable. After all, an atom, unlike the primeval "atom," is a physical system located in space. The term works much better if one takes *a-tom* in the original Greek etymological sense: that which cannot be "cut," meaning that the universe, not "located" anywhere, is unique and inseparable.

Lemaître's reasoning was based on his wish to use the new knowledge of atomic physics and to link nebulae to the atoms, as he wrote it. Compared to his model of 1927, which proposed a slow cosmic evolution, Lemaître from now on proposed a fast cosmology with an explosive origin, which, starting from what is simplest, generated the complex.

No one has thought and defended with such force this conception of the beginning of the world: "We can conceive that space began with the primeval atom and that the beginning of space marked the beginning of time."[42]

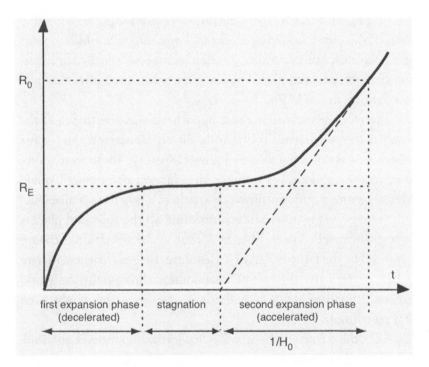

Figure 11.1.

Lemaître's "hesitating universe." The tangent (the diagonal dashed line) to the expansion curve measured today (i.e., the current expansion rate) gives the Hubble time, often considered as an estimator of the age of the universe. One sees clearly how the introduction of a cosmological constant and a stagnation phase invalidates this estimate.

But because Lemaître first published his primeval-atom model in French and in a semi-popular journal unknown to most physicists and astronomers, it took some time until his article was noticed. When it became known, it was poorly received by the majority of scientists. The fact that Lemaître was a mathematician more than an astronomer, together with his religious convictions, no doubt added to their natural resistance towards such revolutionary ideas. One may also wonder whether the literary quality of his work actually undermined its scientific credibility in the eyes of a community little accustomed to such a poetic way of writing about science. Even today, many scientists look askance at works of "popularization."

Eddington never accepted the primeval-atom hypothesis or other ideas of the universe having an abrupt beginning a few billion years ago. Like most other scientists, he felt uneasy about a created universe, and this attitude was shared by the large majority of physicists and astronomers in the 1930s.

Therefore, even if Lemaître's hypothesis was mentioned at the time in the writing of Tolman, de Sitter, Robertson, and some others, it was not embraced as a physical reality. There were, however, a few exceptions. For instance, the Harvard astronomer Donald Menzel wrote a quite enthusiastic article in a popular science journal. "Out of a single, bursting atom came all the suns and planets of our universe!" Menzel began. "That is the sensational theory advanced by the famous Abbé G. Lemaître, Belgian mathematician. It has aroused the interest of astronomers throughout the world because, startling as the hypothesis is, it explains many observed and puzzling facts."[43]

Also, the quantum physicist Pascual Jordan supported Lemaître's model in a 1936 book.[44]

As for Einstein, as early as 1931 and probably unaware of Lemaître's hypothesis, he derived from the Friedmann equations a cyclic cosmological model in which the universe started expanding from $R = 0$ and contracted into a "big crunch," but he considered the appearance of the singularity $R = 0$ to have no physical significance.[45] Later on, when he learned about the primeval atom hypothesis, he considered it as inspired by the Christian doctrine of creation and totally unjustified from the physical point of view.[46]

Lemaître, for his part, remained hopeful that the tide would turn in his favor.

12. Cosmological
Regression (1932)

Give me an atom and I will construct a universe out of it.
—Georges Lemaître[1]

WHEN EINSTEIN HAD TO ADMIT THE EXPERIMENTAL FACT OF space expansion, he bitterly regretted having introduced the cosmological constant. From then on he would not be spared a certain feeling of failure—as, for example, in 1930, when Arthur Eddington demonstrated the instability of the static model, in that a small perturbation is sufficient for the radius of Einstein's hypersphere to become variable over time.

In 1931, in his article "On the Cosmological Problem in the Theory of General Relativity,"[2] Einstein definitively recognized the importance of Friedmann's work for the description of the universe following Hubble's observational data, but he did not quote Lemaître. In 1932, he wrote, "The discovery of the expansion of extra-galactic nebulae justifies the shift to dynamic solutions for the structure of space, a step which heretofore would have appeared to be an expedient justified only by theoretical necessity."[3]

That same year, Einstein and de Sitter—the two promoters of static universe models—joined forces to "catch up" with the competition. They published a one-page paper entitled "On the Relation between the Expansion and the Mean Density of the Universe,"[4] arguing that an expanding universe was also possible without introducing spatial curvature, pressure, or a cosmological constant.[5] It is only required, they claimed, that the density of matter be exactly equal to the critical value that separates the spherical case (positive curvature) from the hyperbolic case (negative curvature).

With historical hindsight, this article represents a singular blunder compared to the calculations advanced by Friedmann, Lemaître, and Robertson. Friedmann and Lemaître had already shown that an expanding universe was possible, with or without a cosmological constant and a negative spatial curvature. The zero-curvature case $k=0$ had been described by Robertson in 1929 in the context of spatially homogeneous and isotropic metrics.[6] The Einstein-de Sitter model too belonged to the class of universes with a singular beginning, with $R = 0$ for $t = 0$, but the authors did not mention this feature, and did not even refer to either Friedmann or Lemaître, but to Otto Heckman.[7] After that, Einstein forsook research in cosmology.

Even so, their article came at the right time. With its two prestigious authors, it lifted the spirits of many scientists who preferred to see Friedmann and Lemaître's profound solutions buried and forgotten—so much so that, for several decades, the scientific press would regularly publish "scoops" on an alleged incompatibility between the Big Bang theory and the age of the oldest stars, based solely on Einstein-de Sitter's ultra-simplified solution.

Big Bang Still Alive and Kicking

As has been mentioned, the value of the Hubble parameter H_0 initially determined by the American astronomer was wrong. In fact, it was about eight times greater than the value measured today. The Hubble error was due to an erroneous estimation of distances to other galaxies. As early as the 1930s, the Dutch astronomer Jan H. Oort had suggested a revision of intergalactic distances, and the German astronomer A. Behr, in 1948, showed that observations indicated that the distance should be double what was previously thought.[8] This increased the calculated date of the Big Bang from 1.8 to 3.5 billion years.

The values of these new distances would be accepted only with the work of Walter Baade in 1952 and Allan Sandage in 1958. The upward revision of the distance scale, and thus the downward revision of the Hubble constant, played a considerable role in the revival of Big Bang cosmology. Indeed, from the value of the rate of expansion initially proposed by Hubble, the age of the universe, calculated within the framework of Einstein-de Sitter's model, was much less than the age of the Earth. The hypothesis of the expansion of the universe therefore seemed less than credible unless it adopted Lemaître's model with the cosmological constant—which astrophysicists were not prepared to do.

It is remarkable that, until very recently, the unconditional opponents of the Big Bang—often for extra-scientific reasons—focused on a hypothetical incompatibility between the theoretical age of the universe (calculated from the rate of expansion) and the age of the oldest objects in the universe (not the Earth, but the oldest stars).[9] In this confrontation, some values of the parameters on which the theoretical age of the universe depends—for example, the ratio of the real density to the critical density and the cosmological constant—were forgotten. Since many cosmologists had long assumed that density was equal to the critical density, for a concoction of reasons that mixed history (the Einstein-de Sitter model being used as a reference), simplicity (calculation being easier), and fashion (the theory of inflation[10]), the opponents of the Big Bang announced with great fanfare the death of that model, immediately relayed by a press eager for sensational news.

It is indeed more interesting to announce to the general public that a famous (though misunderstood) theory has been slain, than to admit that in light of observations, it holds up well within some "error bars." How many articles in the popular science press have been written about the "death of the Big Bang"? Now, if Einstein-de Sitter's ultra-simplified model with critical density and zero cosmological constant is indeed discarded by current observations, the latest experimental data obtained by the WMAP and Planck satellites[11] provide an age of the universe of 13.7 billion years, while the oldest stars in the universe are independently dated at 13 billion years. Thus, the *generic* Big Bang models (with curvature and cosmological constant) come out *strengthened* by the confrontation between the theoretical and experimental ages.

The article by Einstein and de Sitter at least had the merit of raising the question of the existence of large amounts of dark matter. Indeed, the observations available at the time indicated a density of luminous matter much lower than the critical density required by the model, which implied the presence of non-luminous forms of matter. The authors, however, did not discuss this fundamental issue at all.

Density and Debate

The precise balance between the real density of the universe and the critical density derived from theory was the subject of much controversy until the 1980s. Inflation models, developed since then, suggest a "flat" space, which implies, in the absence of a cosmological constant, a density of matter equal to the critical density. However, astronomical observations on the density of matter—visible or dark—favor a universe of clearly subcritical density (thus a hyperbolic space).

The debate has revived dramatically with observations made from 1998 onwards of supernovae (exploding stars) located in distant galaxies, highlighting an accelerated rate of expansion of the universe.[12] The researchers deduced that the total energy density was very close to the critical density, with only a one-third contribution from "ordinary" matter-energy. This means that cosmic energy is essentially in an additional form of the "cosmological constant" type, whose dynamic role is to accelerate cosmic expansion (instead of slowing it down as matter does), thus confirming the framework proposed by Lemaître as early as 1931.

Lemaître Holds Fast

Despite the arguments presented by Einstein and de Sitter, Lemaître retained his original views. In August 1932, when he embarked for the second time on a ship bound for America, Lemaître was preceded by a well-established reputation. His May 1931 letter to *Nature* had made him interesting to the press,[13] with the *New York Times* following it with an article headlined, "Le Maître Suggests One, Single, Great Atom, Embracing All Energy, Started the Universe."

At the time, the Western world was going through the throes of the Great Depression. The media tried to cheer up their readers with exciting, sometimes exaggerated reports on spectacular scientific discoveries. Lemaître became a minor celebrity. On February 19, 1933, the *Times* devoted a long article to Lemaître, stating that he was "one of the leading mathematical physicists of our time," and that his expanding universe became so popular that Einstein's static model seemed "now as obsolete as the quill pen." These media ramblings might have displeased Einstein, but he didn't hold it against Lemaître. In fact, Einstein was beginning to realize that he had been a bit hasty in rejecting the priest's ideas.

Discussions between Einstein and Lemaître

The first meeting between Lemaître and Einstein in Pasadena, California, was more successful than their previous meeting in Brussels in 1927. At that time, Einstein was thinking of leaving Germany to emigrate to the United States. The King and Queen of Belgium, Albert and Elisabeth, sympathized with Einstein, and the name Lemaître, associated with his idea of an expanding universe, had sometimes been mentioned during conversations between the physicist and the royal couple. Thus, in Pasadena, Einstein no longer met a young unknown scientist, but a man whose new ideas were much talked about.

Einstein admitted the reality of expansion as a consequence of general relativity, through Lemaître's cosmological model, which was able to predict Hubble's law. Einstein preferred not to discuss the hypothesis of the primeval atom, because he suspected the Belgian priest of not being scientifically objective on the question. He judged it to be "inspired by the Christian dogma of creation, and unjustified in terms of physics."[14]

The conversation was therefore devoted to the cosmological constant. The situation might well have been disorienting to Einstein. After years of reticence about dynamic solutions, Einstein had finally given in to Friedmann's arguments and, in his article with de Sitter, denied the cosmological constant. (Recall that Friedmann was willing to accept the constant but showed that it did not preclude an expanding universe, which was what Einstein had wanted it to do). But in Lemaître's conversation with Einstein in Pasadena, he argued that, on the contrary, this constant had to be preserved. Lemaître was keen on keeping the cosmological constant because, as we have seen, dynamical models without a cosmological constant produce a universe that is too young.

Figure 12.1.
Albert Einstein and Georges Lemaître in Pasadena, California, 1933.

The exchanges between Einstein and Lemaître were recounted in a picturesque way, full of human warmth, by Lemaître himself, in a text read on Belgian national radio April 27, 1957, marking the second anniversary of Einstein's death.[15] Lemaître told how the journalists who followed their conversations in Pasadena spoke of a "little lamb" which followed them everywhere. In Einstein's original article, the cosmological constant was indeed represented by the Greek letter *lambda*.[16] André Deprit explains that Lemaître had not grasped the joke: the journalists were referring to a well-known American nursery rhyme, "Mary Had a Little Lamb."[17]

In the same text, Lemaître said of Einstein, "No more than others, on subjects that were much more important to him... I was not able to convince him or, I must confess, to grasp his thoughts in a very specific way."

One might add, conversely, that the father of relativity never grasped Lemaître's cosmological thought. The German physicist never ceased to regret the superfluous and abominable character of the cosmological constant, while the Belgian priest constantly repeated to him that the idea, on the contrary, was genius, but "without knowing it." That was because the cosmological constant was indispensable to ensure the adequacy of relativistic models to observations.

But as Lemaître noted in the radio show text, and as the 1947 correspondence between the two men testifies (see Appendix 3), he was unable to convince Einstein. And thanks to Einstein's strong influence, the cosmological constant was abandoned between about 1945 and 1990, after which it made a strong comeback, for it is both a logical necessity and an observational necessity.

Einstein did thaw on one aspect of Lemaître's model: the primeval atom. In January of 1933 Lemaître gave a seminar at the Mount Wilson Observatory in California in which the idea of the primeval atom was discussed. At the end of Lemaître's lecture, Einstein stood up, applauded, and said, "This is the most beautiful and satisfactory explanation of creation to which I have ever listened."[18]

Einstein and Lemaître met again the same year in May, in Brussels. To help Einstein in his political difficulties, the Belgian priest organized, with the support of the Francqui Foundation, a series of scientific conferences led by the father of relativity. Einstein had arrived in Antwerp a few weeks earlier and had learned of Hitler's accession to power. He had renounced his German nationality by handing in his passport at the German Embassy in Brussels, and had resigned from the Prussian Academy and the University of Berlin. Supported in particular by Queen Elisabeth of Belgium, he had settled temporarily in a villa in De Haan (Le Coq),[19] where Lemaître went to visit him to inform him of the proposal of the Francqui Foundation.

Einstein's lectures took place at the University Foundation of Brussels, surrounded by strict security measures. At the penultimate seminar, Einstein announced without prior notice that the next and last seminar would be led by Lemaître, "who has some interesting things to tell us." Four days later, Lemaître explained his ideas and was interrupted several times by Einstein exclaiming, "Very nice, very, very nice!"

Einstein would again show his esteem for his Belgian colleague by supporting his candidacy for the important Francqui prize, which was awarded to Lemaître in March 1934.[20]

13. Black Holes, Fading Space, and the Strangeness of the Universe (1933–1960)

*In fact, the end of the world, like its very beginning, is our conception
of the world. It is in us that landscapes find a landscape. That's why,
if I imagine them, I create them; if I create them, they exist.*
—Fernando Pessoa, *The Book of Intranquility* (1988)

L EMAÎTRE GAVE HIS COSMOLOGY A MORE STRUCTURED FORM IN
1933, published in French as "L'Univers en expansion" in the
Annales de la Société Scientifique de Bruxelles.[1] This very unusual paper
contains many little-known pearls amid various considerations dealing with general relativity as well as various cosmological models,
the formation of galaxy clusters, and the occurrence of singularities.

Black Holes

In his 1933 paper Lemaître demonstrated for the first time that the
apparent singularity of Karl Schwarzschild's solution was only a ficti-
tious one, resulting from a bad choice in the coordinate system.

As early as 1916, Schwarzschild discovered the space-time metric
describing the static gravitational field generated by a spherical mass
without rotation, in vacuum. This solution became singular (in the sense
that some space-time coordinates became infinite) for a non-zero value
of the radius, called critical radius ($r = 2GM/c^2$, where M is the mass,

G the gravitational constant, and *c* the speed of light). For this radius to be physically reached, it was necessary to consider a gravitational collapse of matter leading to extremely compact configurations. This radius was the one already calculated in the eighteenth century by John Michell and later Pierre-Simon Laplace to predict the existence of invisible stars, in the context of the Newtonian theory of universal attraction. These infinities horrified many physicists.[2] Eddington, in particular, called the critical radius a "magic circle within which no measure can lead us," and denied any physical relevance to the concept of gravitational collapse.

In his 1933 article, Lemaître was the first to recognize that what would be called in the 1960s a "black hole" is not a true singularity, and that the only reason infinite quantities seemed to exist there was a bad choice in the coordinate system. To prove his claim, he built an equivalent coordinate system, where these infinities disappear. Unfortunately, the article was published only in French, instead of being published separately in English, and went unnoticed. Thus the development of the relativistic black hole theory would remain blocked for thirty years. The artificial character of Schwarzschild's singularity would only be rediscovered in the 1960s, when the fascinating relativistic models of black holes took off.[3]

The Fading of Space

In this same 1933 article, Lemaître brilliantly dealt with the problem of "space fading," that is, the cancellation of the space radius at the cosmological singularity. His motivation was to discuss the plausibility of the cyclical solution proposed by Friedmann, also studied by Richard Tolman.[4] Normally, Friedmann's closed model begins and ends in a singularity, but Friedmann had suggested the possibility of a cyclical solution where the closed universe successively expands and contracts a large number of times.[5] If we accept certain "exotic" equations of states of matter, we obtain a solution where the space radius oscillates between a minimum value (maximum compression state) and a maximum value (minimum compression state).

According to Tolman, singularities had to be replaced by very small and very dense configurations, like the primeval atom. Lemaître called this model the "phoenix universe" and demonstrated that singularities were inevitable unless quantum corrections were introduced into general relativity. To do this, it was necessary to examine whether the closed solution could be mathematically extended beyond the initial and final singularities—in other words, Lemaître said, "if there is a way to smooth out the cusp of the cycloid" (perhaps better translated "blunt the tip" of it).

Lemaître then sketched a crucial demonstration that cosmological singularities are an inevitable consequence of general relativity under reasonable assumptions. In particular, he demonstrated that neither non-zero pressure nor space anisotropy can prevent the occurrence of a singularity.[6] He thus anticipated the famous "singularity theorems," which were redemonstrated in a more general way in the 1960s and which made their authors, Roger Penrose and Stephen Hawking, famous.[7] Lemaître concluded that the fading of space had to be treated as a real beginning, in the sense that any astronomical structure of a previous existence would have been completely destroyed. It was therefore necessary to abandon the solutions of the cyclical universe, despite their having "an indisputable poetic charm and made one think of the phoenix of the legend."[8]

Vacuum Energy and Background Radiation

Lemaître gave a remarkable follow-up to his "Expanding Universe" in a paper published, in English this time, in the *Proceedings of the National Academy of Sciences (USA)* on January 1, 1934 (previously read before the Academy on November 20, 1933).[9]

Lemaître was at the height of his intellectual powers, as the introduction shows:

> The problem of the universe is essentially an application of the law of gravitation to a region of extremely low density. The mean density of matter up to a distance of some ten millions of light years from us is of the order of 10^{-30} g/cm^3; if all the atoms of the

stars were equally distributed through space there would be about one atom per cubic yard, or the total energy would be that of an equilibrium radiation at the temperature of liquid hydrogen. The theory of relativity points out the possibility of a modification of the law of gravitation under such extreme conditions. It suggests that, when we identify gravitational mass and energy, we have to introduce a constant. Everything happens as though the energy *in vacuo* would be different from zero. In order that absolute motion, i.e., motion relative to vacuum, may not be detected, we must associate a pressure $p = -\rho c^2$ to the energy density ρc^2 of vacuum. This is essentially the meaning of the cosmical constant λ which corresponds to a negative density of vacuum ρ_0 according to

$$\rho_0 = \frac{\lambda c^2}{4\pi G} \cong 10^{-27} \text{g/cm}^3.$$

Lemaître was thus the first physicist to calculate the energy of the vacuum and to associate a negative pressure with it in order to interpret the cosmological constant. He would come back to this question in a later text for the *Japanese Catholic Encyclopedia*. It was only in 1967 that the Soviet physicist Yacov Zeldovich showed that in the light of quantum field theory, the incorporation of λ in the stress-energy tensor can be not only formally but physically justified;[10] indeed, the quantum vacuum makes a contribution to the stress-energy tensor of the form $T_{ij}(\text{vac}) = -(\lambda/8\pi G)g_{ij}$. Lemaître's depth of view and his early insight on the problem of the cosmological constant unfortunately remain ignored by most historians.[11]

Lemaître also suggested that the present universe should be immersed in a bath of equilibrium radiation (i.e., black body) at a temperature equal to that of liquid hydrogen. This temperature is 20 K. Can we deduce from this that Lemaître anticipated the existence of a cosmic background radiation, the residue of the explosion of the primeval atom? Or was it simply an illustration to help the reader grasp the order of magnitude of the coldness of the current universe? The historian's caution prevents us from deciding. If we opt for the first hypothesis, we can say that Lemaître arrived here ahead of the calculation that would make Gamow famous. (See Chapter 16.) However, Lemaître never came back to this point. Instead, he later favored a different type of residual radiation, that of cosmic rays.

Another remarkable element of the 1934 article is Lemaître's reiterated choice in favor of a space with a positive curvature that is not reduced to the simply connected hypersphere, but to the "elliptical space," a multi-connected variant obtained from the hypersphere by identifying the antipodal points. (See Chapter 17.)

The Strangeness of the Universe

The Strangeness of the Universe is a later text, a transcript of a lecture Lemaître gave at the Circle of Rome on January 8, 1960, published in *Revue Générale Belge*.[12] We find again the visionary Belgian commenting on the role of the quantum vacuum in the acceleration of cosmic expansion. In his conclusion, he goes so far as to evoke the hypothesis of a universe with additional dimensions—a subject of research that would later become a burning issue with the theories of superstrings and "brane" cosmologies.

Lemaître comments:

As Einstein himself pointed out and as the great French mathematician Elie Cartan demonstrated with all rigor, the logic of theory leads to equations of which Newton's law of attraction expresses only one particular aspect. Next to the Newtonian term, characterized by the constant of gravitation, is another term dependent on another constant, called the *cosmological constant*. Next to the law of universal attraction, and its force varying as the inverse of the square of distances, there is another equally universal force, attraction or repulsion, which varies like distance. It is easy to understand how this force indicated by the theory would have escaped observation. Contrary to the Newtonian attraction, it is all the weaker the smaller the distances are, it may be insignificant at the distance from the sun or the planets, and yet prove to be dominant at large distances on the scale of the Cosmos. Therefore it is called cosmic repulsion depending on the value of the cosmological constant.

But why bother with a cosmological constant at all? Why not, as Einstein suggested, simply remove it?

Einstein himself expressed the opinion that it would be simpler to remove the cosmological constant and that there was not sufficient reason to maintain it. Einstein's prestige and authority naturally attracted more than one echo.

But removing the cosmological term from the equations, is this really a solution to the difficulty? Isn't it instead following the policy of burying one's head in the sand? Isn't it giving arbitrarily to the cosmological constant a particular value: zero? Isn't it risking to lightly dismiss the possibilities offered by theory to meet and interpret astronomical facts?

In further defending the cosmological constant, Lemaître suggests a parallel with Riemann's radius of space:

The cosmological constant is certainly superfluous to explain gravitation, but gravitation is not all physics. From a purely geometrical point of view, Riemann's radius of space was also a superfluous constant; it was an indication that geometry should not be self-sufficient, but should merge into a larger synthesis, precisely in the geometrical theory of gravitation. Isn't the cosmological constant that appears in the latter theory an indication of a further broadening of the theory in the sense of what Eddington called a fundamental theory, a theory that would succeed in uniting and synthesizing the point of view of the theory of relativity and that of quantum mechanics where a characteristic constant also appears: the Planck constant, which is perhaps not unrelated to the cosmological constant?

This seems to us to be the cosmological constant. While I understand the aesthetic considerations that led Einstein to deny it and to try to make people forget it by equating it with zero, I for my part prefer to take advantage of it in applications, without waiting for its profound meaning to be elucidated.

The Belgian then summarizes his model of a three-stage expansion and underscores a strange feature of our universe:

> I am led to agree with a solution to Friedmann's equation where the radius of space starts from zero with infinite speed, slows down and passes through the unstable equilibrium of Einstein's universe before expanding at an accelerated rate.... In the past, it was said, nature abhors a vacuum; today the physical world is full of it; there is hardly any more than emptiness, with here and there unimaginably reduced singularities where all reality seems to have taken refuge.

Then, after pointing up another strangeness, namely the reigning quantum model of the atomic world, Lemaître drops the bomb:

> Doesn't the strangeness of the current description of the atomic world stem from the fact that we are trying to fit into the narrow space of our sensitive intuition a universe with a much greater number of dimensions? Might not the Universe be a spinor of a space with a few hundred dimensions?
> Who knows?
> Who can say how far Science will take us in discovering the strangeness of the world?[13]

14. The Primeval Atom
Hypothesis (1945)

The assumption of absolute Unity in the primordial
Particle includes that of infinite divisibility.
—Edgar Allen Poe, *Eureka*, a prose poem (1848)

L EMAÎTRE WANTED TO GIVE AN EXPERIMENTAL BASIS TO HIS
hypothesis of the primeval atom, and he believed that cosmic
rays could provide evidence of the initial fragmentation. He deepened
his inquiry in partnership with collaborators such as Odon Godart
(1913–1996)[1] and Manuel Sandoval Vallarta (1899–1977). Lemaître
had met the latter during his stay at Harvard in 1924, and they became friends. Unfortunately, their work together failed to boost the
credibility of the primeval-atom model.[2]

Moreover, the Second World War cut Lemaître off from all relations outside the University of Louvain. At the end of the conflict,
Lemaître withdrew from both the public and the international scientific spotlight. Whereas he had been a tireless traveler in the 1930s, he
now preferred a peaceful life in Louvain, and rarely traveled abroad.
For example, when in 1951 he was offered a visiting professorship at
the Institute for Advanced Studies in Dublin, he declined the invitation. Moreover, even though he still regularly gave lectures in Europe,
Lemaître was by then only remotely interested in cosmology. His new
scientific passion was numerical computation on machines, a field in
which he would also prove to be ahead of his time.[3]

But in the period immediately following the end of the war, he hadn't yet moved on from his cosmological model. "The Primeval Atom Hypothesis" is the text of a lecture Lemaître gave at the annual session of the Swiss Society of Natural Sciences in Fribourg in September 1945, and published the same year in the proceedings of this society. Several other publications of Lemaître appeared under the same title, notably the work that would make Lemaître best known in Europe and abroad: "*L'hypothèse de l'atome primitif: Essai de cosmogonie*," published in Neuchâtel and Brussels in 1946, translated into English in 1950 as *The Primeval Atom: An Essay on Cosmogony*, with a foreword to the English edition by Henry Norris Russel, Professor at Princeton University.[4]

In fact, the 1946 book (excerpts of which we examined in Chapter 11) was not a new text by Lemaître, but a collection of five of his previous articles. Chapter 1, entitled "The Size of Space," is the text of a lecture given on January 31, 1929, at the Scientific Society of Brussels and published in the *Revue des Questions Scientifiques* in March 1929. Chapter 2, entitled "Expansion," reproduces the article "*L'expansion de l'espace*," published in the *Revue des Questions Scientifiques* in November 1931. (See Chapter 13.) Chapter 3, entitled "Evolution," is the text of a public reading before the Royal Academy of Belgium on December 15, 1934, published under the title "*L'Univers en Expansion*" in the *Bulletin de l'Académie* in December 1934. Chapter 4, entitled "Cosmogonic Hypothesis," is the text of the lecture of the same name given at the Royal Belgian Society of Engineers and Industrialists, in Brussels on January 10, 1945, and published in *Ciel et Terre* in March-April 1945. Finally, Chapter 5 takes up the 1945 text, which gives its title to the work.[5] Lemaître wrote a brief additional introduction, as well as about twenty pages of mathematical clarifications in the appendix. The whole was prefaced by Ferdinand Gonseth.[6]

The publication of the book was not timed to maximum advantage, as the theory of the primeval atom was no longer in fashion. In the absence of decisive experimental evidence, it came up against two rival theories. One was a resurgence of Newtonian cosmology. Curiously, Newtonian gravitation was not used for cosmology until after the birth of relativistic cosmology. It was in 1934 that Edward Milne and W. McCrea published papers in which the recession speed of galaxies was explained by a real motion of galaxies in a static and infinite Newtonian background space.[7] Indeed, Milne rejected general relativity and virulently opposed the concept of expanding space. He refused to attribute to space (which according to him had no existence in itself) the properties of curvature and expansion. He therefore developed his own theory in a Newtonian framework, called "kinematic relativity." About expanding space, he wrote:

> This concept, although mathematically significant, has by itself no physical content; it is merely the choice of a particular mathematical apparatus for describing and analysing phenomena. An alternative procedure is to choose a static space, as in ordinary physics, and analyse the expansion-phenomenon as actual motions in this space.[8]

But above all, since 1948, the cosmological theory of the "steady state" had been triumphant, whose main promoters were the American Thomas Gold and the British Hermann Bondi and Fred Hoyle.[9] Their idea was that the universe had always been and will always be as it is now, identical to itself over time (hence the name "steady state"). But since cosmic matter is dispersed by the flight of galaxies, the authors of the steady state proposed that, in order to compensate for dilution and to ensure a constant average density, matter was created spontaneously and continuously—hence the name also given to this theory: "continuous creation."

At the time, as Dominque Lambert notes, "there were no observations able to confirm the existence of a high density state of the universe in the past. The primeval atom hypothesis was thus rejected by a great number of physicists."[10] Materialists saw an additional reason for rejecting Lemaître's hypothesis. They believed that it implied the action of God as creator of the cosmos. That was the case with Bondi, Hoyle, and Gold, who developed their steady-state cosmology assuming an expanding universe without beginning or end. Curiously, in order to avoid what they identified as a "creation" at the beginning of the world, they postulated an ongoing and entirely hypothetical creation of matter that was not supported by any observation or deduced from any serious theoretical framework. It was introduced only to serve their materialist vision of the eternity of the universe.

As noted by Lambert, the materialist position of Fred Hoyle was criticized by the director of the Vatican Observatory, Giovanni Stein, in a 1951 paper entitled "*Creazione senza creatore?*," emphasizing the problems of introducing an unjustified process of matter creation which looked like a kind of *Deus ex machina*.[11] Stein's paper certainly influenced Pius XII when he wrote the discourse *Un'ora* on November 22, 1951. (See Chapter 10.)

Ironically, it was the fiercest opponent of the theory of the primeval atom, Fred Hoyle, who introduced the term "Big Bang." That was on March 28, 1949, when he gave a twenty-minute talk on his new cosmological steady-state theory in a BBC program.[12] A full transcript was printed in the BBC magazine *The Listener*.[13] Having described the basics of the steady-state theory, Hoyle contrasted it with theories based on "the hypothesis that all the matter of the universe was created in one big bang at a particular time in the remote past." This usage, the origin of the cosmological term "Big Bang," has become one of the most successful scientific neologisms ever. Hoyle made clear that he found this kind of theory unacceptable on both scientific and philosophical grounds, in particular because, as he saw it, the big bang creation process was "irrational" and outside science: "I cannot see any good reason for preferring the big bang idea," he concluded. One year later, in the British edition of *The Nature of the Universe*, Hoyle referred twice to the Big Bang.[14]

Hoyle, with his strong personality, did not treat his scientific opponents tenderly. Although Hoyle was a friend of Lemaître (sometimes they went on holidays together in Italy), at a meeting in Pasadena in 1960, Hoyle mocked the Belgian priest, who had become a little fat, by welcoming him with these words: "This is the Big Bang man." But in one of those twists of history, Hoyle would end up contributing to Lemaître's theory twice over: first by coining the term that allowed it to stick in the popular imagination, and more substantively, by contributing to the resolution of the question of the abundance of chemical elements in the universe, a resolution that dovetailed neatly with Lemaître's cosmological model. (See Chapter 16.)

But before this the idea of a hot, explosive beginning of the universe was to gain a more decisive boost from an American of Russian origin, a former student of Friedmann: George Gamow.

15. George Gamow
(1904–1968)

Gamow was fantastic in his ideas. He was right, he was wrong.
More often wrong than right. Always interesting.

—Edward Teller[1]

George Antonovich Gamow, nicknamed "Geo" by his friends, was born on March 4, 1904, in the Black Sea port of Odessa. He took up astronomy as a boy, observing the night sky with a small telescope that his father, a secondary school teacher, had given him for his thirteenth birthday.

Gamow decided on science as a career and pursued mathematics, physics, and astronomy at the University of Odessa from 1922 to 1923. From 1923 to 1929 he continued his University of Leningrad studies. He had Alexander Friedmann as a professor and could attend the lessons on general relativity and cosmology given by Friedmann and Frederiks. During this period he attended a summer school in Göttingen and began exploring whether quantum theory, already successful in explaining atomic structure, could also be applied to the description of the atomic nucleus.[2] Gamow succeeded in explaining the hitherto mysterious phenomenon of natural radioactivity, as well as Lord Rutherford's experiments on the induced transformation of light elements. Thanks to these results, he obtained his doctorate from the University of Leningrad.

From 1928 to 1929 he was in residence at the Institute of Theoretical Physics in Copenhagen, where Niels Bohr had obtained a scholarship for him from the Royal Danish Academy. There Gamow proposed the hypothesis that atomic nuclei can be treated as small droplets of what he called "nuclear fluid." These conceptions are the basis of the theory of nuclear fission later developed by Niels Bohr and John Wheeler.

In 1929–1930, on the recommendation of Niels Bohr, Gamow was awarded a Rockefeller Fellowship at the University of Cambridge. In collaboration with Friedrich Houtermans and Robert Atkinson, Gamow applied his formula for calculating the rate of induced nuclear transformations to the description of thermonuclear reactions taking place inside the sun and stars. This so-called "Gamow formula," first developed for astronomical objects, is now used in the fabrication of hydrogen bombs, as well as in feasibility studies of controlled nuclear fusion.

In 1931 Gamow was recalled to the Soviet Union to take up a chair at the University of Leningrad. In 1933 he obtained permission to leave the country to go to the Solvay Congress in Brussels, and immediately took the opportunity to move to the West. He worked for a time at the Pierre Curie Institute in Paris, then at the University of London. In the summer of 1934 he was invited to lecture at the University of Michigan, and from then on he never left the United States, of which he became a citizen a few years later.

Appointed a professor at George Washington University, he collaborated with Edward Teller on the theory of beta disintegration. He also tirelessly developed the theory of the internal structure of giant red stars; with the Brazilian Mario Schoenberg he demonstrated the role of neutrinos in the loss of energy from stars—a phenomenon called the "Urca process," named after a casino in Rio de Janeiro where people lost money very quickly. Then, with Ralph Alpher, he did his most important work in nuclear physics, explaining the origin of chemical elements through the process of successive neutron captures.

In 1954, then a visiting professor at the University of California, Berkeley, Gamow became interested in biological phenomena after reading the famous article by Francis Crick and James Watson describing the double helix structure of DNA. He then published articles on the storage and transfer of information in the living cell, and proposed a mathematical model of the "genetic code," linking the structure of DNA to the existence of twenty amino acids. From 1956 until his death on August 19, 1968, he was a professor at the University of Colorado. Just before he died, he was quoted as saying, "Finally, my liver is presenting the bill," summing up a life of cheerful intemperance in eating and drinking.

Figure 15.1.

George Gamow, a Soviet and American cosmologist who studied under Alexander Friedmann and was a key, early developer of Georges Lemaître's Big Bang theory.

Throughout his career, the versatile Gamow published extensively and signed articles with such prestigious collaborators as James Chadwick (Nobel Prize, 1935), Lev Landau (Nobel Prize, 1962), Edward Teller, and Charles Critchfield. During the years when Gamow was a successful physicist, he was also celebrated as a writer. He published a number of popular books, some of which featured an original character, Mr. Tompkins, a modest bank clerk whom Gamow used as a Candide-like figure to explain his own theories. Gamow was able to explain complex and difficult concepts in a simple way, using mathematics only when absolutely necessary. His book *Tompkins in Wonderland*, which popularized the theory of relativity in a picturesque way, entertained many readers.[3] He also wrote his autobiography, *My World Line*, published posthumously.[4]

Gamow made a major contribution to astronomy through his work on stellar evolution, building upon Hans Bethe's stellar model. (According to Bethe's thinking, heat and radiation are generated in the cores of stars by thermonuclear reactions, and a star heats up—instead of cooling down—as its fuel runs out.) Gamow also developed the theory of the internal structure of red giants.

But Gamow's most famous contribution to astrophysics is the decisive development he provided for Georges Lemaître's theory of the primeval universe.

16. The Primeval
Substance (1948)

And creation works stubbornly!
—Jules Laforgue, "Autobiographical Preludes" (1885)[1]

G EORGE GAMOW PAID TRIBUTE TO GEORGES LEMAÎTRE IN HIS
1952 book *The Creation of the Universe*:

> The close correlation between the observed phenomenon of expan-
> sion and certain mathematical consequences of Einstein's general
> theory of relativity was first recognized by an imaginative Belgian
> scientist, Abbé Georges Édouard Lemaître, who formulated an
> ambitious program for explaining the highly complex structure of
> the universe known to us today as the result of successive stages of
> differentiation which must have taken place as a concomitant of the
> expansion of the originally homogeneous primordial material. If and
> when such a program is carried through in all details, we shall have a
> complete system of cosmogony that will satisfy the principal aim of
> science by reducing the observed complexity of natural phenomena
> to the smallest possible number of initial assumptions. Although
> such a program is far from completion as of today, considerable
> progress has been made on various parts of it, and the end seems to
> be already in sight.[2]

Although the Belgian scientist laid the foundations of evolutionary cosmology with his work between 1927 and 1934, what would
be dubbed *the Big Bang theory* only fully coalesced in 1948, with

the model of the hot radiative universe developed by Gamow and his collaborators.

Lemaître had imagined that the early universe must have been very dense. Gamow and his collaborators considerably enriched Lemaître's hypothesis by adding the notion of *temperature:* the primordial universe must also have been very hot. This new temperature parameter is the real link between cosmology and high-energy particle physics, disciplines that today work together and whose marriage Lemaître had foreseen as early as 1931.

Curiously, and despite his reference to Lemaître, Gamow credited Friedmann with having introduced the concept of a hot and dense beginning of the universe, writing, "According to Friedmann's original theory of the expanding universe, it must have started with a 'singular state' at which the density and temperature of matter were practically infinite."[3]

More oddly still, Gamow read his own theory into the one of his former teacher: Friedmann's theory of 1922 had nothing to say about the density and temperature of the early universe or of any of its physical properties.

Now let's take a step-by-step look at the progress of Gamow's work.[4]

As early as 1942, Gamow was fascinated by the emerging model of energy generation in stars as developed by Bethe, von Weizsäcker, and Teller. For him, it was clear that the equilibrium processes necessary to form the elements did not work in stars. Gamow gave a lecture at the Washington Academy of Sciences, during which he proposed for the first time the concept of a superdense primordial object composed of nuclear matter that fragments (as in the theory of the primeval atom), but in which the heavy elements are produced by neutron capture reactions. Gamow published his ideas in 1946, within the framework of the cosmological models of Friedmann and Lemaître.[5] Using the then-available data from nuclear physics, developed for military purposes, he proposed a complete theory of the origin of the elements: according to him, *all* the elements of the universe were produced during the first extremely hot phases of the expanding universe.

The same year, Ralph Alpher began his PhD work under Gamow on the subject of primordial nucleosynthesis. They published their first calculation in an article in *The Physical Review*, which became famous as the so-called αβγ, or Alpher–Bethe–Gamow, paper.[6] Gamow's sense of humor is evident from his adding Bethe's name to the list of signatories, without even having asked the opinion of the latter, who had in no way collaborated with them. He explained his joke this way:

> The results of these calculations were first announced in a letter to *The Physical Review*, April 1, 1948. This was signed Alpher, Bethe and Gamow, and is often referred to as the "alphabetical article." It seemed unfair to the Greek alphabet to have the article signed by Alpher and Gamow only, and so the name of Dr. Hans A. Bethe (*in absentia*) was inserted in preparing the manuscript for print. Dr. Bethe, who received a copy of the manuscript, did not object, and, as a matter of fact, was quite helpful in subsequent discussions. There was, however, a rumor that later, when the α, β, γ theory went temporarily on the rocks, Dr. Bethe seriously considered changing his name to Zacharias.[7]

The difficulty Gamow alludes to is the fact that the primordial nucleosynthesis process stopped at the formation of the lightest elements (deuterium, helium, lithium) and did not produce carbon or the other heavy elements, which reduced their hope of explaining the origin of *all* chemical elements by the early hot universe. Moreover, the paper did not consider any consequence of a primordial universe dominated by radiation.

In an article he prepared the same year for the journal *Nature*, Gamow tried to set the conditions of the primordial universe by considering only the formation of deuterons and at the same time the problem of galaxy formation.

In the meantime, Robert Herman joined Alpher to begin a collaboration that would last several decades. In the summer of 1948, Gamow sent Alpher and Herman the manuscript of the article he had already submitted to *Nature*. They noticed errors in the manuscript and sent them by telegram to Gamow, who was spending the summer in Los Alamos. Gamow was aware that it was too late to make the necessary corrections, and with great scientific probity, urged Alpher and Herman to submit their own article to *Nature*. He even went so far as to give *Nature*'s editor advance warning and asked him to publish Alpher and Herman's comments as soon as possible after his own article. Gamow's article appeared on October 30, 1948, and Alpher and Herman's on November 13.[8]

It was in this short correction occupying a thin column of the journal that Alpher and Herman took a decisive step for modern cosmology. Continuing Gamow's calculations, they calculated that, at a time later than that of nucleosynthesis, when the universe cooled to a few thousand degrees, it suddenly became transparent and let out its "first light." Alpher and Hermann predicted that this residual temperature should be received today in the form of "black body" radiation cooled by expansion to the temperature of 5 K.

It was also Alpher who, in another article the same year, introduced the term *Ylem* (borrowed from Aristotle) to describe the first substance from which the elements were supposed to have formed. Let us recall that it was the following year, 1949, that Hoyle used the term "Big Bang" for the first time, during a radio broadcast.

The background temperature results were discussed in much more detail in a series of publications by Alpher and Herman from 1949 to 1951. The calculation made in the last paper gave a too-high value of 28 K, due to new values adopted for the density of the universe. In 1950 Gamow independently published an article in *Physics Today* predicting fossil radiation at a temperature of 3 K, without giving any explanation. In 1953, he estimated a temperature of 7 K, and in 1956 a new value of 6 K, without ever making detailed calculations as Alpher and Herman had done.

Curiously, in none of these three articles did Gamow refer to the more precise work of his collaborators, which subsequently introduced confusion as to the correct attribution of the fossil radiation prediction. Scientists by no means read all the literature, the volume of which is enormous, and tend to prefer to follow articles by very "well known" authors. As we have seen, the same phenomenon has notably occurred to the benefit of Edwin Hubble and to the detriment of Georges

Lemaître with regard to the discovery of the expansion of the universe and the law of the recession of galaxies.

In any case, the beginning of the 1950s was unfavorable to the supporters of the Big Bang, because the theoretical age of the universe estimated in the simplifying framework of Einstein-de Sitter's model was too short compared to the age of the oldest stars (as discussed in Chapter 12). The steady-state model was then at the height of its popularity.

In 1952, Gamow concluded his popular work *The Creation of the Universe* with this hazy image of the creation of the world:

> In the dim pregalactic past we perceive a glimpse of a metaphysical "St. Augustine's Era" when the universe, whatever it was made of, was involved in a gigantic collapse. Of course, we have no information about that era, which could have lasted from the minus infinity of time to about five billion years ago, since all "archaeological records" pertaining to that distant past have been completely obliterated when the cosmic masses were squeezed into a pulp. The masses of the universe must have emerged from the Big Squeeze in a completely broken-up state, forming the primordial *Ylem* of neutrons, protons, and electrons. As the *Ylem* cooled rapidly through expansion, these elementary particles began to stick to one another, forming aggregates of different complexities which were the prototypes of the atomic nuclei of today. During this early period of "nuclear cooking," which lasted not more than an hour of time, conditions throughout the universe closely approximated those existing in the center of an exploding atomic bomb. Cosmic space was full of high-energy gamma radiation, the mass-density of which exceeded the density of ordinary atomic matter. The temperature throughout the universe was in the neighborhood of 10^9 degrees, but the density of matter was comparable to the density of atmospheric air at high altitudes.
>
> Following that highly productive first hour of the history of our universe, nothing in particular happened for the next 30 million years.[9]

In comparison with current astrophysical data,[10] we note that due to an overestimation of the Hubble parameter—and a corresponding underestimation of the age of the universe—the time scales given by Gamow are skewed: one hour instead of three minutes for the epoch of primordial nucleosynthesis, thirty million years instead of 400,000 years for the epoch of fossil radiation emission, and three billion years instead of fourteen billion for the age of the universe.

Regarding the chemical abundances calculated in the framework of primordial nucleosynthesis, the calculations in the famous "αβγ paper" were improved upon in later articles, especially those by Alpher, James Follin, and Herman in 1953.[11] Gamow named the curves giving the values of elemental abundances and temperatures as a function of the time elapsed since the Big Bang the "Divine Creation Curves." In the years that followed he used them in his letterhead.[12]

Such calculations continued until the 1970s, as new experimental data and improved computer programs became available. Two schools of nuclear astrophysicists clashed. One, led by Alpher and Gamow, championing the creation of all the elements in the primordial universe. The other, led by Hoyle, championed the creation of all the elements in the heart of the stars within the framework of a stationary universe.

In the end neither camp got it all their way. In 1964 Hoyle and R. J. Tayler recognized that the formation of helium was an insurmountable problem for the steady-state model, thus strengthening the case for Lemaître's Big Bang model.[13] At the same time, it eventually became clear that not all the elements arose in the primordial universe, per Alpher and Gamow. Today we know that only the lightest isotopes—hydrogen, deuterium, helium, lithium—could have been formed in the warm universe at its origin, according to the process understood by Gamow; the heavier elements, such as carbon, nitrogen, oxygen, etc., were formed in a much more recent era, in the heart of stars where the conditions of temperature and density necessary for the fusion of helium are met for a sufficiently long time.[14]

As emphasized by Dominique Lambert, according to Lemaître, all the elements (H, He, etc.) had been produced by successive disintegrations of the primeval atom, and Lemaître clung to this mistaken idea all his life, despite the results coming from particle and nuclear physics, and despite advice given him by some of his Louvain colleagues, such as Charles Manneback (who had studied with Bohr, Heisenberg, and Fermi). This may have been partly due to Lemaître holding these fields at arm's length because they were not sufficiently unified for his taste, his having once jokingly compared elementary particle physics to entomology. In 1948, Teller traveled to Brussels for the eighth Solvay Confernce to present work that Gamow, Maria Goeppert-Mayer, and he had produced, which included a description of the early universe as a sphere filled with neutrons that generated, via beta decay, first protons and later the light nuclei. Lemaître declined the invitation to discuss the subject with Teller.[15]

The Discovery of Fossil Radiation

In the mid-1960s, at Princeton University, theorists Robert Dicke, James Peebles, Peter Roll, and David Wilkinson took up the concept of the "phoenix-universe" developed by Tolman and Lemaître, in which the contracting space, rather than being infinitely crushed (the "Big Crunch"), passes through a minimum radius before bouncing back for a new cycle. They calculated that this "hot bounce" would generate a black body radiation measurable today at a temperature of 10 K. Then they learned that such radiation had just been detected, by chance, at the Bell Labs in New Jersey. Physicists Arno Penzias and Robert Wilson developed an astronomical radiometer there and found a higher-than-expected background noise at a wavelength of 7.35 cm: after deducting antenna noise and absorption by the atmosphere, an excess temperature of 3.5 K remained.

Observers and theorists agreed on a simultaneous publication of their respective results in two articles, published in the July 1965 issue of the *Astrophysical Journal*.[16] Penzias and Wilson gave only the results of their measurements, while, in the second article, Dicke, Peebles, Roll, and Wilkinson offered their cosmological interpretation. None mentioned the predictions of Alpher, Herman, and Gamow, let alone those of Lemaître! Note also that Dicke et al. did not use the term Big Bang, opting instead for the term "primordial fireball."

It was Lemaître's close collaborator Odon Godart who told him of the experimental discovery of fossil radiation—which Lemaître had elegantly called "the vanished brilliance of the origin of the worlds."[17] The priest had been taken to the hospital in Louvain for a heart problem. Godart later recalled that Lemaître was at the same time happy because the relics of the primeval atom had been discovered, but a bit sad too because the fossil radiation was not made of cosmic rays as he had expected.[18] Lemaître died a few months later, on June 20, 1966, from leukemia. The fact is that the primeval atom hypothesis was finally becoming, under the more media-friendly name of the Big Bang, a physical theory in its own right.

Ironically, Penzias and Wilson, at the time of their discovery, believed in Hoyle's steady-state theory rather than that of the Big Bang. However, the detection of the fossil radiation practically signed the death sentence for Hoyle's model. Relating the discovery of background radiation, Robert Wilson would later write:

> Arno and I of course were very happy to have any sort of an answer to our dilemma. Any reasonable explanation would have probably made us happy. In fact, I do not think that either of us took the cosmology very seriously at first. We had been used to the idea of steady-state cosmology; I had come from Caltech and had been there during many of Fred Hoyle's visits. Philosophically, I liked the steady-state cosmology. So I thought that we should report our result as a simple measurement: the measurement might be true after the cosmology was no longer true![19]

In 1967, Gamow, Alpher, and Herman began to despair about how much their seminal work was being ignored. Gamow took the initiative to write a journal article that appeared in the *Proceedings of the National Academy of Sciences*.[20] Correct attributions finally began to gradually emerge after this publication, until Steven Weinberg, in his famous popularized book *The First Three Minutes*, finally made the matter clear because he had consulted the original sources (which scientists rarely do, making do with second- or third-hand information and thus continuing to propagate historical misattributions).[21]

In 1975, armed with new measurements on cosmological parameters (expansion rate of 55 km/s/Mpc and material density equal to

6 percent of the critical density), Alpher and Herman confirmed the value of 2.7 K for the fossil radiation.[22]

At the beginning of the 1990s, millimeter-wave data collected by the Cosmic Background Explorer (COBE) satellite made it possible to fix the temperature of cosmological radiation with great precision, at 2.736 ± 0.017 K, and to detect for the first time the minute variations in temperature from one region of the sky to another, linked to fluctuations in density marking the origin of all large-scale astronomical structures, from galaxies to galaxy clusters and superclusters.

In February 2003, the Wilkinson Microwave Anisotropy Probe (WMAP) satellite brought observational cosmology into a period of experimental renewal, where high-precision observations made it possible to measure the values of the parameters of the universe to within a few percentage points—measurements confirmed and refined by the European Planck telescope in the subsequent decade. All these measurements provide a strong experimental basis for the Big Bang theory.[23]

One wonders why the predictions of Gamow, Alpher, and Herman about fossil radiation, although published by the most widely read and reputable scientific journals, were not taken more seriously. Why, Weinberg asks, were no systematic searches for this radiation undertaken before 1965? The technology was available, but no one saw the need for such measurements. Until 1964, the seeming success of stellar nucleosynthesis appeard to eliminate the need for primordial nucleosynthesis, a conclusion that weighed in favor of the cosmological steady-state model. Also, communication between experimenters and theorists was poor: theorists did not know that radiation at very low temperatures was experimentally detectable, and experimenters did not know that fossil radiation from the early universe had been predicted to exist. Finally, physicists found it difficult to take cosmology seriously; many thought that speculations about the early universe were purely fanciful.[24]

Here is how severe the communication problem was: the first measurement of fossil radiation had been obtained indirectly a quarter of a century earlier, but went unnoticed. In a series of publications between

1937 and 1943, Theodore Dunham and Walter Adams reported the discovery of interstellar absorption lines in the optical domain—later identified with the molecules CH and CN.[25] Using these data, Andrew McKellar had calculated in 1941 that these lines must come from excited states at a temperature of 2.3 K, but he attributed this temperature not to background radiation, but to collisions between electrons.[26]

Honor Where Honor Is Due

One may question the motivations of some researchers. Integrity is one of the most important aspects of science. Some unscrupulous researchers (often those who do not have a significant discovery to their credit) may claim that the correct attribution of discoveries does not matter, that only the advancement of science counts. This attitude certainly does not reflect the ideals and realities of the scientific enterprise. The accuracy of the history of science must be scrupulously respected, especially since this is a recent history, with all the texts and related documents available to all.

The Nobel Prize in Physics was awarded to Arno Penzias and Robert Wilson on December 8, 1978. Lemaître and Gamow had died a decade earlier. For the theoretical side, James Peebles was awarded the Nobel Prize only in 2019, at the age of 84. It is interesting to note that, in an interview given just after he accepted the prize, Peebles, who had been one of the very few American cosmologists to recognize Lemaître's contributions as early as the 1960s, declared his dislike of the term "Big Bang":

> The first thing to understand about my field is that its name, Big Bang theory, is quite inappropriate. It connotes the notion of an event and a position, both of which are quite wrong.… It's very unfortunate that one thinks of the beginning whereas in fact, we have no good theory of such a thing as the beginning.…
>
> I have given up, I use Big Bang, I dislike it. But for years, some of us have tried to persuade the community to find a better term without success. So "Big Bang" it is. It's unfortunate, but everyone knows that name. So I give up.[27]

Peebles, as we have seen, was not alone in having strong reservations about the eminently catchy label "Big Bang." But was he really on solid ground in insisting that the theory does not describe a beginning, or even an event? The question is here left for the reader.

17. The Topology of the Universe (1900–present)

The eternal silence of these infinite spaces terrifies me.
BLAISE PASCAL, *PENSÉES* (1670)

I WILL CONCLUDE THIS DESCRIPTION OF THE WORK OF THE FATHERS of the Big Bang theory by examining one of their contributions that, curiously enough, has hardly been noticed by other commentators, but that nevertheless constitutes one of the most remarkable signs of their originality. That is: the topology of space. Indeed, Friedmann and Lemaître not only looked at cosmic dynamics, but also at the overall structure of the universe, i.e., its topology. (I am not including Gamow, who came from the field of nuclear physics and was not trained in advanced mathematics and geometry.) Moreover, both Friedmann and Lemaître quickly became aware of the incompleteness of the theory of general relativity as regards this problem.

One of the oldest cosmological questions is that of the extension of space. Is it finite or infinite? Newtonian physical space, mathematically identified with infinite euclidean space, is not without some paradoxes, such as the Olbers's paradox, and boundary condition problems.[1] If we refer for example to Mach's principle, which guided Einstein in the elaboration of general relativity, and according to which local inertia would be the result of the contributions of masses (stars, planets, black holes, etc.) to infinity, an obvious problem of divergence arises. This is because infinite space, if it is homogeneous (that is, filled with matter in roughly the way the visible universe is), has an infinite mass.

Einstein's Aesthetics and Finite Space

When Einstein introduced a three-dimensional space of positive curvature—the hypersphere—into his cosmological model of 1917, one of his main motivations was to provide a model of finite space, albeit without boundaries. This solution so ingeniously solved all the paradoxes related to Newtonian space that most cosmologists at the time accepted the new idea, while neglecting other possibilities.

Einstein also thought that the hypersphere provided not only the metric of space—that is, its local geometric properties—but also its global structure, its *topology*: for example, the fact that the volume of space is finite. The question of the global shape of space, or more generally of its finite or infinite character, is not only a matter of metrics; it is above all a matter of topology, and as such requires an additional approach to that of Riemannian differential geometry—the mathematical support of general relativity.

Since Einstein's equations are partial differential equations, they describe only the local geometric properties of space-time. These properties are contained in the metric tensor, which allows us to calculate the components of the curvature at each point in space-time. But Einstein's equations do not fix the global structure of space-time: for a given metric, the solution of the equations corresponds to several— and even generally an infinity—of topologically distinct models of the universe.

Mathematically, a space is said to have a *simply connected* topology if, at each of its points, any closed curve can be continuously contracted at a point;[2] this is the case, for example, with the infinite euclidean plane or the surface of a sphere. Otherwise, the topology is said to be *multiconnected*. Any surface that has, for example, a hole (such as a torus or a sphere with a handle) is multiconnected.

For a given metric, the simplest topology is that of the simply connected space having this metric locally. But mathematical simplification rarely warrants a secure conclusion of physical relevance. For instance the Riemannian manifolds are less "simple" than the euclidean space, but they are more relevant for describing gravity in general relativity. So what can guide the physicist's choice of topology?

In the era of pre-relativistic cosmology, the German astronomer Karl Schwarzschild had already shown an astonishing topological intuition. It is evident in the postscript of an article he published in 1900:

> One could imagine that as a result of enormously extended astronomical experience, the entire universe consists of countless identical copies of our Milky Way, that the infinite space can be partitioned into cubes, each containing an exactly identical copy of our Milky Way. Would we really cling to the assumption of infinitely many identical repetitions of the same world? In order to see how absurd this is, consider the implication that we ourselves as observing subjects would have to be present in infinitely many copies. We would be much happier with the view that these repetitions are illusory, that in reality space has peculiar connection properties so that if we leave any one cube through a side, then we immediately reenter it through the opposite side.[3]

This description is that of a hypertoric space, suggesting that spiral nebulae (which at the time had not yet been identified as galaxies external to ours) are only ghost images of our own Milky Way, due to a particular topological structure of space.

Karl Schwarzschild was one of those visionary astronomers with a deep mathematical background. Since Riemann's seminal work, nineteenth-century mathematicians had begun to discover examples of finite volume but borderless spaces. Among them is the hypertorus, consisting of a single parallelepipedal block of euclidean space reconnected to itself, so that everything that passes through one face reappears at a point on the opposite face. But, in the eyes of all, this closed space was a pure abstraction, with no relation to physical space.

Arguing with Einstein

Topology was not one of Einstein's concerns. His 1917 article does not mention any topological alternative to his spherical space model. In a March 1917 letter to Willem de Sitter, he jokingly wrote, "We philosophize… [about whether the universe] extends infinitely, or has a finite size and is a closed unit. Heine has provided the answer in a poem: 'And a fool waits for an answer.'"[4]

However, Einstein claimed to give a definitive answer in favor of the closed universe, with his hypersphere model. Immediately, some of his colleagues, more aware of recent developments in topology, pointed out to him the arbitrary nature of his choice. De Sitter, in his famous cosmological article of 1917, noted that Einstein's cosmological solution admitted a different form of spherical space: that of three-dimensional projective space (also called "elliptical space"), constructed from the sphere by identifying diametrically opposite points. This space has the same metrics as the spherical space, but a different topology—in particular its volume is half as large:

> There are two possible forms of space with constant positive curvature, namely spherical space, or space of Riemann, and the elliptical space, which has been investigated by Newcomb. In the spherical space all straight lines[5] starting from a point intersect again in the "antipodal" point, whose distance from the first point measured along any of these lines is πR. In the elliptical space, any two straight lines cannot have more than one point in common. In both forms of space the straight line is closed: its total length is $2\pi R$ in the spherical space, and πR in the elliptical space. In the spherical space the largest possible distance between two points is πR, and there is only one point, the "antipodal" point, at that distance from a given point. In the elliptical space the largest possible distance is $(1/2)\,\pi R$, and all points at that distance from a given point lie on a straight line—the "polar line" of the point. Both spaces are finite. The total volume of the spherical space is $2\pi^2 R^3$, and of the elliptical space $\pi^2 R^3$.
>
> Einstein only mentions the spherical space, which by the two-dimensional analogy of the sphere is easier to represent to our imagination. The elliptical space is, however, really the simpler case, and it is preferable to adopt this for the physical world.[6]

And de Sitter adds as a note: "This is also the opinion of Einstein (communicated to the writer by letter)."

This note by de Sitter is surprising, because Einstein clearly took the side of spherical space in his discussions with other interlocutors.

Thus, when Hermann Weyl[7] also wrote to him on the question of the choice between spherical or elliptical topologies, Einstein answered him in a letter dated June 1918:

Now to the question: spherical or elliptic. I do not think that there is a possibility of really deciding this question through speculative means. A vague feeling leads me to prefer the spherical one, though. For I sense that those manifolds are the simplest in which *any closed curve can be contracted continuously to one point.* Other people must have this feeling as well; since otherwise the case where our space could be euclidean and finite would surely also have been taken into consideration in astronomy. The two-dimensional euclidean space would then have the connectivity properties of an annulus. It is a euclidean plane, on which every phenomenon is doubly periodic, where points lying on the same period grid are identical. In a finite euclidean space there would be three kinds of closed curves not continuously reducible to one point. Analogously, an elliptic space, in contrast to the spherical one, possesses one sort that cannot be contracted continuously to one point; that is why it appeals to me less than the spherical one.

Can it be proved that the elliptic space is the only variety of the spherical space that can be obtained through the addition of periodicity properties? It seems to be so.[8]

Einstein repeated this argument in a postcard dated April 16, 1919, this time addressed to Felix Klein[9]:

I would like to relay to you an argument that allows the spherical option to appear preferable to the elliptic one. In the spherical world every closed line can be contracted continuously into one point, but not in the elliptic one; i.e., only the spherical, not the elliptic, world is simply connected.... In addition to the euclidean metric element, there are, of course, also *finite* spaces of arbitrary size that can be obtained from infinity by postulating a threefold periodicity,[10] if it is further postulated that periodically lying points are identical. These possibilities, which incidentally do not apply in the case of general relativity, suffer from the characteristic that these spaces are connected in multiple ways.[11]

Thus, without further physical argumentation, Einstein had an "aesthetic" bias in favor of the simply connected character of space.

In his answer to Weyl, Einstein was notably mistaken on the last point: in addition to elliptical space, in three dimensions, there are an infinite number of topological variants of spherical space, all closed, including so-called "lenticular" spaces, "prismatic" spaces, and "polyhedral" spaces[12] (whereas for two-dimensional surfaces with positive curvature, there are in fact only two distinct topological types, the sphere and the elliptical plane). But nobody knew this yet. The topological classification of three-dimensional spaces was only just beginning to be understood.

Three-Dimensional Euclidean Space

The study of the different forms of three-dimensional euclidean space began with crystallography. The Russian Evgraf Fedorov classified the eighteen symmetry groups for crystalline structures in $\mathbb{R}^3$ in 1885; and in 1911, Ludwig Bieberbach developed a theory of crystallographic groups.[13] However, it was only in 1934 that Werner Nowacki would demonstrate how the crystallographic groups give rise to the topologies of euclidean space.[14] The case of spherical spaces was posed by Felix Klein in 1890 and by Wilhelm Killing in 1891, under the name of the Clifford-Klein problem.[15] This problem was completely solved in 1930 by William Threlfall and Herbert Seifert,[16] and made intelligible to non-mathematicians only in 2001, with a view to applying it to cosmology.[17]

As for the problem of hyperbolic homogeneous spaces, classification only began to be seriously addressed in the 1970s by William Thurston.[18] Developed in particular by Jeffrey Weeks,[19] it is now the subject of intensive research.

The historical relationship between topology and cosmology thus contrasts with the relationship between non-euclidean geometry and general relativity. Non-euclidean geometry and tensor calculus in Riemannian space were well developed at the time when physicists needed them to model gravitation; on the other hand, the pioneers of relativistic cosmology who wanted to take topology into account in their models of the universe initially had little to glean from mathematics.

The discovery of non-static solutions by Friedmann in 1922, and by Lemaître in 1927, considerably enriched the field of cosmological modeling. Homogeneous and isotropic universe models admit spherical, euclidean, or hyperbolic spaces depending on whether their spatial curvature (constant) is positive, zero, or negative. In his popularizing book *The World as Space and Time*, Friedmann mentions the topological problem and insists on the fact that metrics, and thus general relativity, are not sufficient on their own to define the global structure of space. In order to decide this, "additional assumptions" are needed. In particular, he gives the example of the cylinder; this two-dimensional surface is a topological variant of the euclidean plane obtained by identifying the opposite edges of a flat strip of infinite length. The cylinder is indeed a locally euclidean surface (its curvature is everywhere zero), but it is finite in one direction and infinite in the other. As Friedmann wrote:

> This discussion on the structure of the world cannot end without mentioning an unfounded assertion that is repeated not only in popular books and articles, but also in some of the more serious and specialized articles on the theory of relativity. I am referring to the problem of the *finitude* of the world, in this case the finitude of our starry space.[20]
>
> It is commonly said that if the world has a positive constant curvature, we can conclude that it is finite—first that a straight line has a finite length, that the volume of the world is finite, and so on. This conclusion is based either on confusion or on additional assumptions. *It does not derive in any way from the equations of the world*, only the metric can be deduced from these equations. Simple examples can show this. The metric of the surface of a cylinder and the metric of the plane are identical, but on the cylinder there are "straight lines" of finite length (the circle), whereas there is no finite straight line in the plane. The problem of the finitude of space depends not only on the metric, but also on the condition that two coordinate systems define one point and one point only.[21] However, this condition is rather arbitrary; even reasonable restrictions,

which we will not discuss here, leave open the question of whether some points in space are identical to other points or not.[22] Thus, metrics alone cannot solve the question of the *finitude of* space;[23] additional theoretical and experimental considerations are needed to solve this problem. Certainly, under some conditions, one can hope to solve the problem of the finitude of space.

For example, suppose that a people of shadows living on the surface of a sphere try to solve this question; to do so, they could send one of their members to travel on the sphere; by moving always in a straight line and in a given direction, the traveler, observing the aspect of the landscape, could notice that it changes; he would see other landscapes, and visit other spherical cities, different from those of his native country; but after some time, the traveler would notice that the landscape around him becomes more and more similar to the one he left at the beginning of his long journey, and he would realize that he returns to his city of departure by the opposite end. At the end of his journey, meticulous observations would lead him to conclude that his point of arrival is absolutely identical to his point of departure; he would thus discover the finitude of his spherical universe; it will have been necessary for him to carry out additional measurements, the metric of the sphere alone could not solve the question of its finitude.

Therefore, the fact that the universe has a constant positive curvature does not necessarily imply that it is finite.[24]

Friedmann errs in one regard here since, as stated in the previous note, all spherical spaces are finite. Friedmann corrected the mistake in his 1924 article. The following sentence would have been correct: "Therefore, the fact that the universe has a constant *negative or zero* curvature does not necessarily imply that it is *infinite.*"

Friedmann's most profound remarks on the topological question can be found in that 1924 article. (The key paragraph is reproduced in Chapter 7.) Friedmann is the first to clearly define the fundamental limitations of cosmological theory based on general relativity. "Einstein's world equations without additional assumptions are not yet sufficient to draw a conclusion on the finiteness of our world," he writes. He focuses on defining how space can become finite if we identify some points of space with other points of space (which, in topological language, makes space multiconnected). He also sees how this possibility allows the existence of "phantoms," in the sense that at the same point an object and its own images coexist. "A space with a positive curvature is always finite," he adds, but mathematical knowledge does not make it possible to "solve the question of finitude for a space with a negative curvature."

Dispelling "the Nightmare of Infinite Space"

As one can see, unlike Einstein, Friedmann is not prejudiced in favor of a simply connected topology, but he believes, like most physicists of the time, that only spaces of finite volume are physically permissible to describe real space. The universe models proposed by Einstein and de Sitter in 1917, and then by Friedmann in 1922, all have a positive curvature and thus satisfy the criterion of finitude. With the negative curvature models proposed by Friedmann in 1924, the problem is more difficult: hyperbolic space, in its simplest version (simply connected topology), extends to infinity. Thus, even at the time of the "creation" of the universe, space itself would have been infinite; in other words, the universe would not have been born at a point, but the expansion would have been triggered at each point of a pre-existing infinite space.

Aware of this difficulty, Friedmann sees a loophole in the fact that Einstein's equations are not sufficient to decide whether space is finite or infinite, even if the curvature is negative or zero. Additional assumptions have to be made to specify boundary conditions, such as whether or not certain points in space are identified with each other. The whole problem of cosmic topology is thus posed, but Friedmann did not have sufficient mathematical developments to continue the discussion.

For his part, Lemaître fully shared the common preference for the finiteness of space, but for a more metaphysical reason. He was confident the universe could be understood by the human mind. Indeed, already in the early 1920s, while at seminary, he expressed his conviction that the universe was intelligible and even adapted to our rational abilities—a view, moreover, in harmony with the Thomistic training that he had received in 1919 at Louvain's Institute of Philosophy.[25]

Was this an exception to his scruples, discussed in Chapter 10, over not letting one's theological beliefs guide scientific conclusions, or did his leanings in this regard merely make it that much easier for him to follow the evidence where it seemed to be leading—namely to a finite universe? Here again I will leave the question for the reader's consideration. But in either case, on this point he was in opposition to seventeenth-century French thinker Blaise Pascal, who viewed space as infinite. In 1958 Lemaître wrote:

> The view we have proposed [the primeval atom hypothesis] may be contrasted with that of Pascal in his *Pensées*. We may reverse Pascal's wording and say that the Universe not being infinite neither in size or in duration, has some proportion to mankind. Science has not to surrender in the face of the Universe, and when Pascal tries to infer the existence of God from the supposed infinitude of Nature, we may think that he is looking in the wrong direction. There is no natural limitation to the power of mind. The Universe does not make an exception, it is outside of our grip.[26]

In a lecture at the Institut Catholique de Paris, in which Lemaître spoke about the development of geometry in the nineteenth century, he described Riemannian geometry as having "dispelled the nightmare of infinite space."[27] All the cosmological models he opted for from 1927 onward assume a space of positive curvature, not only necessarily finite, but with the multiconnected topology of elliptical space. This in no way prevented him from recognizing other possibilities. He was, it seems, the first cosmologist to notice, in 1958, that negative curvature metrics also admit finite volume topologies: "It is true that a locally hyperbolic space is not necessarily open. It is possible to construct such spaces, polytrops, i.e. Klein's forms of finite volume. This is even true for euclidean space."[28]

Lemaître discussed at length the possibility of elliptical space, notably in his 1931 text. Unlike Einstein he preferred it, but like Einstein his argumentation seems to be based largely on "aesthetic feeling."

These extremely fertile ideas about topology remained largely ignored by the general field of cosmology, with a few exceptions. Indeed, cosmologists in the first half of the twentieth century had no experimental means to measure the topology of the universe, just as Gauss and Lobachevski, pioneers of non-euclidean geometries in the mid-nineteenth century, had no means to measure the curvature of space. Thus the great majority of the pioneers of relativistic cosmology lost interest in the question.

The Dark Ages of Topography

When in 1932 Einstein and de Sitter proposed the euclidean model in perpetual expansion (see Chapter 12), they avoided anything that could go against maximum simplicity; they assumed a zero curvature, a zero cosmological constant, and did not even bother to specify that the topology of their model was simply connected. Yet it is this very particular solution that served as the "standard" cosmological model for the next sixty years. These years were therefore the dark ages of cosmic topology. Almost all cosmology textbooks, whether special- ized or not, failed to mention the topological question, reducing the problem of the finite or infinite character of space to its curvature alone. All efforts at observational and theoretical cosmology focused on determining the rate of expansion and curvature of space, implic- itly assuming that the spatial structure of the universe is the finite hypersphere, the infinite euclidean space, or the infinite hyperbolic space, without mentioning the topological alternatives.

This arbitrary simplification led to confusion about the qualifiers "open" and "closed" used to characterize Friedmann's and Lemaître's models. It was believed to apply not only to the time behavior of the models (open if they are in perpetual expansion, closed if they are in expansion-contraction), but also to their spatial character. Assuming a simply connected topology and a zero cosmological constant, there is indeed a strict coincidence between perpetually expanding models and spatially infinite models on the one hand, and between expansion- contraction models and spatially finite models on the other hand. But, according to Friedmann's warning, in order to know whether space is finite or infinite, it is not enough to determine the sign of the spatial curvature, i.e., to compare the density of matter-energy with the critical density; "additional assumptions"—precisely those of topology—are needed.

The two most notable examples of this deceptive simplification are a specialized textbook by Steven Weinberg, which constituted a kind of bible for all students in the 1970s and 1980s, and the popularizing books by George Gamow.[29] Gamow's talent as an educator and humorist captured the imaginations of two generations of readers, to the point of converting some of them to the profession of cosmology. The flip side of the coin is that, by repeatedly asserting that euclidean and hyperbolic spaces are necessarily infinite, Gamow was partly responsible for the profession's lack of interest in cosmic topology.

Bright Lights in the Dark Ages

There were exceptions to the general rule of widespread disinterest in cosmic topology. Some original minds were asserting themselves, first and foremost quantum cosmology theorists, for whom the question of the topology of the universe is of quite natural interest.

Quantum cosmology seeks to understand the mechanism, supposedly of a quantum nature, by which the universe came into existence. These theorists therefore attempt to extend the history of the universe, described by general relativity and Big Bang models, to a time so remote that it is certain that general relativity fails and that quantum generalization becomes necessary.

In the 1960s, physicist John Wheeler was the first to suggest that the topology of space-time can fluctuate at the microscopic level. Scenarios were then born in which the "traditional" Big Bang was replaced by a spontaneous birth of the universe based on random quantum fluctuations. The ultimate ambition of these new approaches was to calculate all the properties of the universe thus created and to reconcile the predicted properties with the observable reality. One of the properties we could thus hope to predict is the topology of space. Nobody was able to carry out the program of quantum cosmology, but at least the interest in topology in the framework of cosmology had been revived.

In 1971, George Ellis published an important article reviewing recent mathematical developments in space classification and their possible applications to cosmology.[30] This led to a renewed interest in the subject, spearheaded by theorists such as the Russian Dimitri Sokoloff, the Brazilian Helio Fagundes, and the Chinese Fang Li-Zhi.[31] An observational program was launched in the Soviet Union, under the direction of Viktor Schvartsman. With the newly installed six-meter diameter telescope at Zelentchuk in the Caucasus, the "phantom sources" Friedmann spoke of in 1924, i.e., multiple images of the same galaxy, were sought. All tests failed: no ghost image of our Milky Way or of a nearby cluster of galaxies was found. This negative result set constraints on the minimum size of a multiconnected space and did not encourage researchers to pursue this type of investigation. Interest in cosmic topology then lapsed until the early 1990s.

Recent Developments

This book, which primarily traces the history of relativistic cosmology across three periods from 1917 to 1965, might well stop here. But, for the curious reader, I will conclude by briefly describing some spectacular and more recent twists and turns the subject has taken. These deal with the size and shape of space, addressing one of the oldest questions of cosmology, whether relativistic or not.

In 1995, a lengthy article entitled "Cosmic Topology" was published in *Physics Reports*.[32] It listed everything that researchers had published on the subject since 1917 (about fifty articles in total), and indicated new and interesting avenues of research, such as the method of "cosmic crystallography."[33] The time was ripe for a renewed interest at the international level, requiring the combined skills of mathematicians, cosmological theorists, and observers. Cosmologists finally had mathematical and experimental tools to test the topology of the universe. Deep surveys of the sky were beginning to deliver the three-dimensional geography of the universe, and the astronomical satellite COBE had just scrutinized in detail the structure of fossil radiation, allowing us to probe the most distant past of the universe.

In the years that followed, the number of articles published on cosmic topology far exceeded all those published in the previous eighty years. The shape of space had become one of the most exciting issues in the discipline.

One result that could prove to be decisive came from the observations of the WMAP satellite. From the tiny temperature fluctuations of this background radiation, scientists can extract a wealth of information such as the energy density of the universe, its material constitution, age, curvature, and overall shape. With previous measurements, less precise than those of WMAP, the density parameter was in a fringe more or less centered around the critical value, seeming to confirm the "standard model" of an infinite euclidean space, in perpetual accelerated expansion under the action of a cosmological constant. But in February 2003, the publication of the first WMAP results indicated that the density parameter (normalized to the critical density) was between 0.99 and 1.04. The value of 1, corresponding to the euclidean universe, was well within the range, but this range also encompassed spherical and hyperbolic cases.

Another WMAP measurement dealt a second blow to the infinite euclidean model. Fluctuations in the fossil radiation are the result of acoustic vibrations that passed through the primordial plasma. It is therefore possible to reconstruct the "music" of the early universe. And the data showed a deficit in the longest wavelengths compared to what is predicted by the model of the infinite universe, as if the lowest notes of the cosmos were missing. Why is this? Maybe because the universe is not large enough to be able to play them, like a guitar string that cannot emit a lower sound than its length and diameter allow.

The absence of very large-scale fluctuations led several research teams to propose space models with multiconnected topology, such as the Poincaré dodecahedral space (positive curvature), the hypertorus (zero curvature), and the Picard space (negative curvature).[34] In all cases it is necessary to imagine the interior of a polyhedron whose faces are glued two by two by specific mathematical transformations, so that when one face is reached, one returns to the polyhedron by the homologous face.[35] These spaces are finite, but without edges and

Figure 17.1.
The Wilkinson Microwave Anisotropy Probe (WMAP) operated from 2001 to 2010. Its purpose was to shed light on the conditions of the early universe by measuring properties of the cosmic microwave background radiation, energy released an estimated 375,000 years after the birth of the universe.

without limits, so we can travel there indefinitely. As a result, one has the impression of living in a vaster space, paved with polyhedra that multiply as in a palace of mirrors. And the return of the light rays that cross the faces produces optical mirages: the same object has several images.

These models are not alternatives to the Big Bang, but versions that reject the idea of infinite space in favor of a physical space whose volume could be a little bit smaller than that of the observed universe, and which contains a finite amount of matter. Each one makes precise predictions: a total density in matter/energy of the universe to within a hundredth, and the existence in fossil radiation of specific signatures. These predictions have recently been put to the test by results obtained in 2013 from the Planck telescope.[36] The dodecahedral model seems to be ruled out, but not the hypertorus or other more complex topologies.[37]

It remains to be noted that the time evolution of these models (accelerated expansion of space) was anticipated by Lemaître in 1931 (upper curves in the diagram in Figure 9.3), while their spatial structure refers to multiconnected topologies.

The field of cosmic topology thus emerged from the shadows; and here again, it is striking that Alexandre Friedmann and Georges Lemaître were pathfinders.

18. Conclusion

*Given that it takes millions of years for some stars to send
us light signals, it is not surprising that the world spends
so many long sleepless nights in absolute darkness.*
—Pierre Dac, *Essays, Maxims and Lectures* (1978)

ALL THE COSMOLOGICAL PROBLEMS DISCUSSED BY FRIEDMANN and Lemaître before 1934, followed by Gamow and his collaborators before 1950, are fundamental problems whose solutions, offered by the "new cosmology" after 1980, are close to those proposed by these three "fathers of the Big Bang."

The following list summarizes some of the key issues in cosmology where their insights have proven fruitful and, in most cases, even decisive.[1] One hopes that history will grant the three all due credit.

- Expansion of space from an initial singularity
- Dominant role of the cosmological constant in cosmic dynamics
- Importance of radiation pressure in the primordial universe
- Role of quantum gravity at the origin of the universe
- Problem of the age of the universe solved with the cosmological constant
- Interpretation of the cosmological constant by quantum vacuum energy
- Possibility of "phoenix universe"

- Existence of relics of the early universe (fossil radiation, ultra-energetic cosmic rays)
- The fact that particles from the primordial universe produced the original stellar matter (hydrogen and helium)
- Role of random primordial density fluctuations in large-scale structure formation (now postulated in the initial Harrison-Zeldovich spectrum)
- Need for computer programs to understand the formation of galaxy clusters
- Role of cosmic magnetic fields
- Non-trivial topology of the universe

On all these questions, Lemaître, in particular, showed an astonishing perspicacity. This is the reason why the astronomer William McCrea, although an adept of Newtonian Milne's cosmology, could declare the following in an article judiciously entitled "Some Lessons for the Future":

> Lemaître was a scientist of superbly robust common sense. All of us who knew him must ever have wished we had paid attention to his ideas.... Einstein, Eddington, and Milne may have been greater scientists than Lemaître, and more famous in their day. But on the subject of cosmology and its importance for astronomy, Lemaître had more to impart. He talked better sense.[2]

Indeed, Lemaître talked better sense. And now, finally, we are listening.

APPENDIX 1.
THE FRIEDMANN-
LEMAÎTRE COSMOLOGICAL
MODELS DEPICTED

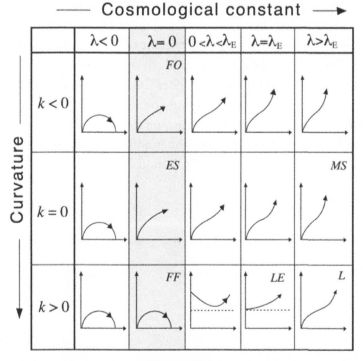

Figure A1.1.

The dynamics of the Friedmann-Lemaître cosmological models, i.e., the variation of the spatial scale factor as a function of cosmic time, are determined by the sign of the (constant) curvature of the spatial sections, k, and by the value of the cosmological constant, λ.

Two critical values of the cosmological constant are $\lambda = 0$ and $\lambda = \lambda_E$, where λ_E is the value proposed in 1917 by Einstein to ensure the staticity of the spherical universe. When $\lambda = 0$, we find the current Friedmann models in the grey column: FO designates the open hyperbolic model, FF the closed spherical model. A special case is the euclidean solution of Einstein-de Sitter, marked ES.

Since a positive cosmological constant is equivalent to a repulsive action at great distance, all models with a large enough cosmological constant ($\lambda > \lambda_E$), whatever their curvature, are "open" in time, i.e., in perpetual expansion. Conversely, a negative constant ($\lambda < 0$) contributes to increasing effective gravity, so that the corresponding models of the universe all end up collapsing in a "Big Crunch."

In some cases ($k > 0$ and $0 < \lambda < \lambda_E$), the initial singularity may disappear; in particular, Lemaître-Eddington's model (marked LE) is a spatially closed universe in continuous expansion from Einstein's static sphere (corresponding to a constant radius indicated in dotted lines). The primordial explosion model advocated by Lemaître (L) has a cosmological constant slightly higher than the critical value λ_E, so that it goes through a more or less long phase during which it borders on Einstein's static state, before returning to continuously accelerated expansion. The current data favor the "standard model" marked MS, but with indications in favor of the L model.

Appendix 2.
Discovering The Big Bang:
A Chronology

1915: Einstein and Hilbert provide the definitive equations of the theory of general relativity.

1917: Einstein derives the first relativistic cosmological model, according to which space is spherical and static, with constant density. Einstein introduces the cosmological constant.

1917: De Sitter derives the second relativistic cosmological model, according to which space is static and empty of matter but with a cosmological constant.

1918: Weyl introduces his ideas on the possible unification of gravitation and electromagnetism.

1920: Shapley and Curtis participate in the "Great Debate" on the extragalactic nature of nebulae.

1922: Friedmann provides the first model of an expanding universe with positive curvature, variable density, non-zero cosmological constant, and zero pressure.

1922: Einstein claims that Friedmann made a miscalculation.

1923: Einstein withdraws his criticism and admits his mistake.

1923: Friedmann publishes *The Universe as Space and Time*.

1923: Weyl suggests the non-static character of de Sitter's universe.

1924: Friedmann gives the first model of a hyperbolic expanding universe. First wide-ranging discussion on cosmic topology.

1924: Eddington indicates that out of forty-one spectral shifts of measured galaxies, thirty-six are red; he favors de Sitter's solution.

1925: Lemaître finds a second form of de Sitter's metric, suggesting an expanding space with zero curvature.

1925: Lemaître demonstrates a linear relationship between distance and spectral shift in de Sitter's solution.

1925: Hubble establishes the scale of extragalactic distances and closes the "Great Debate."

1927: Lemaître proposes a model of an ever-expanding universe with positive curvature, time-varying density and pressure, and a cosmological constant adjusted so that the universe has no beginning. He gives the first interpretation of the redshifts related to the expansion of space and predicts a linear distance-redshift relationship.

1929: Robertson finds the general metric of all spatially homogeneous universes, but does not realize its importance.

1929: Hubble experimentally determines the linear distance-recession velocity relationship, but does not link it to expansion.

1930: Eddington proves the instability of Einstein's universe and adopts Lemaître's model.

1931: Hubble and Humason set the constant of proportionality between recession speed and distance at H_o = 558 km/s/Mpc.

1931: Lemaître proposes his model of an initially singular universe, the primeval atom, after which a phase of stagnation allows the formation of galaxies, followed by a third stage of accelerated expansion. He suggests that cosmic rays are the relics of the primeval universe.

1931: Lemaître proposes a quantum origin of the universe.

1932: In a single-page article, Einstein and de Sitter analyze the simplest case with zero curvature, zero pressure, and zero cosmological constant; they give the relationship between density and rate of expansion.

1933: Lemaître demonstrates the occurrence of singularities in homogeneous anisotropic cosmological models.

1934: Lemaître makes the link between the cosmological constant and the energy of the vacuum.

1945: Lemaître pulls together his cosmological work in *L'hypothèse de l'atome primitif* (*The Primeval Atom Hypothesis*).

1946: Gamow proposes cosmological nucleosynthesis.

1948: Alpher and Gamow calculate the abundances of elements formed in the primeval universe.

1948: Alpher and Herman make the prediction of a cosmic background radiation, in the form of a black body at the temperature of 5 Kelvin.

1952: Baade revises the extragalactic distance scale, which increases the cosmic time scale by a factor of 2.6.

1965: Penzias and Wilson accidentally discover the cosmic microwave background radiation at a temperature of 3 Kelvin. Dicke, Peebles, Roll, and Wilkinson provide a cosmological interpretation in the framework of Big Bang models.

1980: François Englert and Alan Guth propose the inflationary model, a phase of exponential expansion in the very early universe, driven by an unknown scalar field.

1992: The COBE observation satellite checks the thermal nature, homogeneity, and isotropy of the cosmic microwave background radiation to an accuracy of 10^{-5}, and reveals small temperature anisotropies.

1998: First observational clues in favor of an acceleration of cosmic expansion.

2003: WMAP satellite data sets the age of the universe at 13.7 billion years with a spatial curvature close to zero. Hints of a finite, spherical universe with a multiconnected topology.

2013: Planck satellite data reduce measurement uncertainties on various cosmological parameters, and remain compatible with non-zero spatial curvature and multiconnected topology.

2016: The LIGO and Virgo teams jointly announce that they directly detected gravitational waves. The waveform matched general relativity's predictions for a gravitational wave coming from the inward spiral and the merging of two black holes, thus initiating a new branch in cosmology and astrophysics, gravitational-wave astronomy.

2019–2022: Employing very-long-baseline interferometry, the Event Horizon Telescope's collaborative team published the first images of two massive black holes, one at the center of the M87 Galaxy and the other at the center of our Milky Way Galaxy, confirming the existence of black holes and further verifying Einstein's general theory of relativity.

2021: James Webb Space Telescope is launched.

2023: After James Webb Space Telescope observations provide evidence that galaxies formed earlier than predicted, some cosmologists begin questioning the Standard Model of Cosmology.

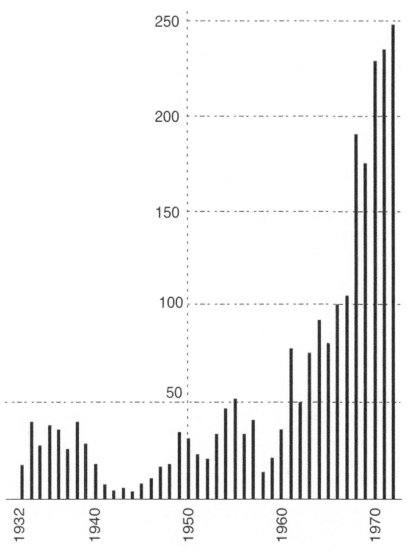

Figure A2.1.

Histogram giving the number of cosmology articles published between 1932 and 1972 (articles listed each year in *Physics Abstracts* under the headings "Cosmology" and "Cosmogony"). The first "wave" (1932–1940) follows the articles by Einstein-de Sitter and Lemaître. The second (1948–1957) is initiated by the work of Gamow and collaborators. The sharp rise from 1965 onwards follows the discovery of fossil radiation. Since then, the number of publications has continued to grow.

APPENDIX 3.
CORRESPONDENCE BETWEEN LEMAÎTRE AND EINSTEIN (1947)

Letter from Lemaître to Einstein, July 30, 1947[1]

Brussels, July 30, 1947

Dear Professor Einstein,

I have been asked to contribute to the volume which will be dedicated to you in the LIBRARY OF LIVING PHILOSOPHERS.[2] I have chosen for [my] subject "The Cosmological Constant," a subject that I have had sometimes the advantage to discuss with you. I remember that the last time I met you at Princeton some of my reasons impressed you somewhat. That is the reason why I make some effort to modify your present attitude against what I always have considered as one of your greatest contribution[s] to Science.

The main points of my paper are

1. that gravitational mass, which has a definite effect, could not have been identified with energy, which is defined but for an additive constant, if theory would not provide some mean[s] of adjustment when the zero level of energy is changed at will.

2. that the cosmological constant is necessary to get a time-scale of evolution which would definitively clear out from the dangerous limit imposed by the known duration of geological ages.

3. that the instability of equilibrium between gravitational attraction and cosmical repulsion is the only mean[s] to understand an evolution on the stellar scale during the short time available of some ten of times the duration of geological ages. All that would be impossible without the cosmological constant.

Whatever will be your attitude in connection with my essay, I would like to say that, in my mind, it is but a tribute of admiration for your work.

With kindest regards,
I am
Yours very sincerely,
G. Lemaître

Letter from Einstein to Lemaître, September 26, 1947[3]

September 26, 1947
Professor G. Lemaître
9 rue Henry de Braekeleer
Brussels, Belgium

Dear Professor Lemaître:

I thank you very much for your kind letter of July 30th. In the meantime I received from Professor Schilpp your interesting paper for his book. I doubt that anybody has so carefully studied the cosmological implications of the theory of relativity as you have. I can also understand that in the shortness of T_0 there exists a reason to try bold extrapolations and hypotheses to avoid contradiction with facts. It is true that the introduction of the Λ term offers a possibility, it may even be that it is the right one.

Since I have introduced this term I had always a bad conscience. But at that time I could see no other possibility to deal with the fact of the existence of a finite mean density of matter. I found it very ugly indeed that the field law of gravitation should be composed of two logically independent terms which are connected by addition. About the justification of such feelings concerning logical simplicity it is difficult to argue. I cannot help to feel it strongly and I am unable to believe that such an ugly thing should be realized in nature.

Your argument 1) for the Λ term I do not find convincing. Since it is known that energy is equal to the inert mass there is no more room for an additive constant of energy.

There is one fundamental point in the theory of relativity which is problematic and may have to do with the problem of the explosion time T_0. The elementary length

$$ds = \sqrt{g_{ik} \, dx_i \, dx_k}$$

is supposed to be an invariant. This is the basis for the whole mathematical theory of gravitation. Besides this it is also assumed that there are uniquely determined physical objects (rods and clocks) which can be used to measure this invariant. This assumption is really used in cosmology by assuming that the period of a certain spectral line in the whole four-dimensional space keeps the same absolute length. This assumption would be fully justified a posteriori if relativistic physics would be developed far enough to get such a "clock" as a perfectly determined solution of the field equations. We are far from such accomplishment so that the hypothesis of the existence of objects for the measurement and comparison of the ds in quite distant parts of space-time can be doubted. I have given more thought to this point but it may be enough to mention it here.

Finally one should not forget that the gravitational equation with the energy tensor on the right side is only a provisional form which has to be substituted finally by an equation for the total field. We can, therefore, not be absolutely sure that this step will not influence the aspect of the cosmological problem. I do, however, not believe that such will be the outcome.

With kind regards, yours sincerely,
Albert Einstein

Letter from Lemaître to Einstein, October 3, 1947

October 3, 1947
9 rue Henri de Braekeleer
Bruxelles

Dear Professor Einstein,

I thank you very much for your kind letter of Sept. 26.

It is with a deep sense of appreciation that I have read your comments on my paper and your views about your own attitude of mind and on some problems involved in the theory of relativity.

Your first point was the "ugliness of the field equations."

These equations may be deduced from some simple principles: 1) gravitation is a manifestation of curvature, 2) matter is a partial manifestation of it, 3) which fulfills some differential equations of conservation.

The equations which result from these principles, which are of a beautiful simplicity, contain an "ugly combination of independent terms." This may be an indication that the theory remains open to new developments which may connect the theoretically unknown value of the cosmical constant with the other constants in physics.[4]

It is true that my first argument is valid only when matter or energy is conceived as something which is conserved and nothing else; then it can be counted from an arbitrary level, with corresponding different values of the cosmical constant.

At a further stage of the theory, energy is identified with inert mass and gravitational mass; then its value is definite. Accordingly, the cosmological constant[5] is no more arbitrary and has a precise value; but there is no a priori reason why this would be zero.

Your third point was the meaning of the ds. I think that the fundamental notion involved is that there is some meaning to conceive of a repetition of the same experiment, so that the same physical causes would produce their effects in the same time.

Relativity insists that, if this has a meaning, the experiment must be supposed to be accomplished along a line of space-time, and the time involved in the formulation of the physical laws must be the proper time $\int ds$ on these lines.

Therefore, if a number of experiments [are] once started and finished together, then, if the same experiments are repeated somewhere else and started together, they will finish together. Any instrument which repeats indefinitely the same experiment and counts the number of experiments performed is a clock.

The atoms which absorb light in the sun or in the companion of Sirius or in a distant nebula, behave according to rules which are not explicitly stated in relativity (these absorptions depend on quantum theory) but, if we can convince ourselves that they are the same atoms that we know on earth, then we know that they perform the same experiment and therefore count the proper time.

I believe it would be too exciting a requirement to ask that relativity should be developed far enough to produce a standard clock as a solution of its field equations.

Your last point was that field equations, involving electricity, may modify the cosmological problem. The answer seems to be that cosmological theory uses only a very crude approximation: the Newtonian approximation, therefore minute refinements of the theory could not alter the result. Furthermore, electrical fields cannot have a cumulative effect with distance as gravitation.[6]

With kindest regards, etc.

G. Lemaître

ENDNOTES

1. A Cosmological Crisis (1925–1935)

1. Thomas S. Kuhn, *The Structure of Scientific Revolutions* (Chicago: University of Chicago Press, 1962).

2. See, for example, the collection of the founding texts of Copernicus, Galileo, Kepler, Newton, and Einstein in *On the Shoulders of Giants: The Great Works of Physics and Astronomy*, ed. Stephen Hawking (London: Penguin, 2002).

3. See, for example, Lee Smolin, *Three Roads to Quantum Gravity* (New York: Basic Books, 2002); Jean-Pierre Luminet, *L'écume de l'espace-temps* (France: Odile Jacob, 2020).

4. Nicolaus Copernicus, *De revolutionibus orbium coelestium* (Nuremberg, 1543). English translation: *On the Revolutions*, trans. Edward Rosen (Baltimore, MD: Johns Hopkins University Press, 1992).

5. Tycho Brahe, *Astronomiae instauratae progymnasmata* (Prague, 1603); in *Tychonis Brahe Danis Opera Omnia*, 15 vols., ed. J. L. E. Dreyer (Copenhagen: Libraria Gyldendaliana, 1913–1929). As far as I know there is no available English translation.

6. See, for example, William Boulting, *Giordano Bruno: His Life, Thought, and Martyrdom* (Abingdon-on-Thames, UK: Routledge, 2014).

7. Johannes Kepler, *Astronomia Nova* (1609). See, e.g., William H. Donahue, *Selections from Kepler's Astronomia Nova* (Santa Fe, NM: Green Lion Press, 2004).

8. Galileo Galilei, *Sidereus Nuncius* (The Starry Messenger) (1610). See, e.g., M. Sharratt, *Galileo: Decisive Innovator* (Cambridge, UK: Cambridge University Press, 1994).

9. On the relationship between astronomical revolutions and literature, see Marjorie H. Nicolson, *Science and Imagination* (Ithaca, NY: Great Seal Books/Cornell University Press, 1956).

10. "Wilkinson Microwave Anisotropy Probe," NASA, December 22, 2017, http://map.gsfc.nasa.gov/.

11. "Planck," European Space Agency, http://www.esa.int/Our_Activities/Space_Science/Planck.

12. Jacques Merleau-Ponty, *Cosmologies du XXe siècle* (Paris: Gallimard, 1965), 8. English translation: *The Rebirth of Cosmology*, trans. Bruno Morando (Athens, OH: Ohio University Press, 1982).

13. See for example Bruce Reichenbach, "Cosmological Argument," *Stanford Encyclopedia of Astronomy*, last modified June 30, 2022, https://plato.stanford.edu/entries /cosmological-argument/.

14. As for the collections, *Theories of the Universe: From Babylonian Myth to Modern Science*, ed. Milton K. Munitz (New York: The Free Press, 1957) presents, from Plato's *Timaeus (c.* 355 BC) to Fred Hoyle (1950), a set of texts marking important milestones in the evolution of Western cosmological thought. This collection of cosmological literature includes an article by Lemaître, but none by Friedmann. The relativistic period between 1917 and 1982 is covered in the collections of Jeremy Bernstein and Gerald Feinberg, *Cosmological Constants* (New York: Columbia University Press, 1989) and Kenneth Lang and Owen Gingerich, *A Source Book in Astronomy and Astrophysics, 1900–1975* (Cambridge, MA: Harvard University Press, 2014). As for analyses, I would cite the monumental work of Pierre Duhem, *Le Système du Monde*, for the pre-Copernican period, Alexandre Koyré, *Du monde clos à l'univers infini* and *Etudes Newtoniennes* for the later period and, for cosmologies of the twentieth century, Jacques Merleau-Ponty, *Cosmologies du XXe siècle*, George Ellis, "Cosmology from 1917 to 1960" in *Einstein and the History of General Relativity*, eds. Don Howard and John Stachel (Berlin: Birkhaüser, 1989), and *Modern Cosmology in Retrospect*, eds. B. Bertotti et al. (Cambridge, UK: Cambridge University Press, 1990).

15. Transcribed literally from Russian, the correct spelling would be Fridman; see for example the article by V. Fock, who was his pupil: "The Researches of A. A. Fridman on the Einstein Theory of Gravitation," *Soviet Physics Uspekhi* 6, no. 4 (1964): 473–474. In the 1922 article published in *Zeits. f. Physik*, the spelling is Friedman. It is Einstein who apparently introduced the variant "Friedmann" in his "Remark on the work of A. Friedmann" published the same year in *Zeits. f. Physik*. This spelling prevailed, so much so that the second article by the Russian physicist in *Zeits. f. Physik* in 1924 is signed "Friedmann"! I will therefore adopt here the usual spelling.

16. *Biographical Encyclopedia of Scientists* (Philadelphia: Institute of Physics Publishing, 1994).

17. *Inventeurs et Scientifiques* (Paris: Larousse, 1994).

18. *Dictionary of Scientific Biography*, 16 vol., ed. C. Gillespie (New York: Scribner, 1970–1980).

19. Poincaré's role might be underestimated in the development of the theory of special relativity. See for example A. A. Logunov, "Henri Poincaré and Relativity Theory," *Physics Uspekhi* 47, no. 6 (2004): 607–621 and A. A. Logunov, M. A. Mestvirishvili, and V. A. Petrov, "How Were the Hilbert-Einstein Equations Discovered?," Cornell University ArXiv (2004), https://arxiv.org/abs/physics/0405075.

20. H. P. Robertson, "Relativistic Cosmology," *Reviews of Modern Physics* 5 (January 1933): 62.

21. See the remarkable analysis of Dominique Lambert, *The Atom of the Universe*, trans. Luc Ampleman (Krakow, Poland: Copernicus Center Press, 2015).

22. See for example P. J. E. Peebles, "Impact of Lemaître's Ideas on Modern Cosmology," in *The Big Bang and Georges Lemaître*, ed. André Berger (Dordrecht, the Netherlands: D. Reidel Publishing Company, 1984); Joseph Silk, *The Big Bang* (New

York: Freeman, 1989). It is true that Silk is francophone; as for the 2019 Nobel laureate Peebles, he received the first prize awarded by the Lemaître Foundation in 1994.

23. George Smoot and Keay Davidson, *Wrinkles in Time* (New York: William Morrow, 1993).

24. The term "Big Bang" was introduced in 1949, following a British radio broadcast in which Fred Hoyle, the fiercest opponent of Lemaître's theory and promoter of the alternative theory of the steady-state, used it in derision. Hoyle used the term again in his writings in 1950 (see Chapter 14).

2. GRAVITATION (4TH CENT. BC–1917)

1. For a more complete development, see for example Jean-Pierre Luminet, *Black Holes* (Cambridge, UK: Cambridge University Press, 1992), Part 1, "Gravitation and Light."

2. Aristotle, *Physics*, trans. Robin Waterfield (Oxford, UK: Oxford University Press, 2008).

3. Isaac Newton, *De Philosophiae naturalis principia mathematica* (1687); *The Principia*, trans. I. Bernard Cohen et al. (Los Angeles: University of California Press, 2016).

4. "James Clerk Maxwell, "A Dynamical Theory of the Electromagnetic Field," *Philosophical Transactions of the Royal Society of London*, 155: 459–512 (1864), https://upload.wikimedia.org/wikipedia/commons/1/19/A_Dynamical_Theory _of_the_Electromagnetic_Field.pdf.

5. James Clerk Maxwell, *Treatise on Electricity and Magnetism* (Oxford, UK: Oxford University Press, 1873).

6. H. A. Lorentz, "Over de terugkaatsing van licht door lichamen, die zich bewegen," *Royal Academy of Sciences at Amsterdam*, vol. 1 (1892): 28–31, and "Versuch einer Theorie der electrischen und optischen Erscheinungen in bewegten Körper" (Leiden, the Netherlands: E. J. Brill, 1895). Many of Lorentz's papers are available in English at Proceedings of the Royal Netherlands Academy of Arts and Science, https://dwc.knaw.nl/toegangen/digital-library-knaw/?pagetype=publist&search _author=PE00001670. For Lorentz, the transformation linking universal time to local time was, however, purely formal.

7. For precise references concerning the period after 1900, see *The Collected Papers of Albert Einstein*, made available in digital form by Princeton University Press, https://einsteinpapers.press.princeton.edu/. Texts there are available in both the original German and in English.

8. Henri Poincaré, "Sur la dynamique de l'électron," *Comptes rendus de l'Académie des Sciences* 140 (1905): 1504–1508. The essence of special relativity had already been proposed by Poincaré in various previous communications, and especially in a chapter of his book *La science et l'hypothèse* (Paris, 1902). For an English translation see Henri Poincaré, *Science and Hypothesis*, trans. W. J. G. (UK: Read Books, 2013). Poincaré's work was closely studied by Einstein. See in particular E. T. Whittaker, *A History of the Theories of Aether and Electricity*, vol. 2, *The Modern Theories (1900–1926)*, (Edinburgh, UK: Thomas Nelson and Sons,1953).

9. A. Einstein, "Über den Einfluß der Schwerkraft auf die Ausbreitung des Lichtes" ["On the Influence of Gravity on the Propagation of Light"], *Annalen der Physik* 35 (1911): 898–908. An English translation is available at *Relativity Resources*, last accessed January 2024, http://www.relativitybook.com/resources/Einstein _gravity.html.

10. Gustav Mie (1868–1957) was the first physicist of the twentieth century who tried to build a complete theory of matter. In 1912–1913, while professor of Experimental Physics at the University of Greifswald, Mie wanted to extend Maxwell's electromagnetic theory to the broader framework of special relativity, and proposed that elementary particles were manifestations of a universal electromagnetic field. His goal was to go beyond the traditional opposition between "fields" and "matter" to obtain a unified view of the physical world. His ideas inspired Hilbert's attempt to axiomatize physics.

11. Gregorio Ricci (1853–1925) and Tullio Levi-Civita (1873–1941), Italian mathematicians, introduced the "absolute differential calculus," today called tensor calculus. See G. Ricci and T. Levi-Civita, "Methods of Absolute Differential Calculus and their Applications," *Mathematischen Annalen* 54 (1901): 125–201.

12. Albert Einstein and Marcel Grossmann, "Entwurf einer verallgemeinerten Relativitätstheorie und einer Theorie der Gravitation," *Zeitschrift für Mathematik und Physik 62* (1913): 225-261.

13. Albert Einstein, "Die formale Grundlage der allgemeinen Relativitätstheorie," *Sitzungsberichte der K. Preussischen Akademie der Wissenschaften*, part 2 (Berlin, 1914): 1030–1085.

14. Hilbert preceded Einstein by a few days, with the two papers taking different forms. David Hilbert, "Die Grundlagen der Physik, Nachr. Ges. Wiss. Göttingen," *Math. Phys. KI.*, 395 (presented to the Göttingen Academy Nov. 20, 1915); Albert Einstein, "Die Feldgleichungen der Gravitation," *Sitzungsber. Preuss. Akad. Wiss.* 2 (1915): 844 (presented to the Prussian Academy Nov. 25, 1915).

15. A. Einstein, "Die Feldgleichungen der Gravitation," in *Preussische Akademie der Wissenschaften, Sitzungsberichte* (1915), 844–847.

16. In fact, Emmy Noether's theorem would be demonstrated in 1918 in an article published under her own name. This theorem has become a vital tool in theoretical physics, whose scope is much more general than the initial framework of a theory of gravitation. In 1917, Weyl discovered a particular case of Noether's theorem by deriving identities that had been independently found by Ricci in 1889 and by Bianchi in 1902.

17. A. Einstein, "Die Grundlage der allgemeinen Relativitätstheorie," *Annalen der Physik* 49 (1916): 769–822.

3. Static Cosmologies (1917)

1. Albert Einstein to Paul Ehrenfest, February 4, 1917, in *The Collected Papers of Albert Einstein*, vol. 8, *The Berlin Years: Correspondence, 1914–1918 (English Translation Supplement)*, trans. Ann M. Hentschel (Princeton, NJ: Princeton University Press, 1998), document 294, https://einsteinpapers.press.princeton.edu/vol8-trans/310.

2. Albert Einstein,"Kosmologische Betrachtungen zur allgemeinen Relativitäts-theorie," in *Preussische Akademie der Wissenschaften, Sitzungsberichte* (Berlin, 1917), 142–152. Albert Einstein, "Cosmological Considerations in the General Theory of Relativity," trans. W. Perrett and G. B. Jeffery, in H. A. Lorentz et al., in *The Principle of Relativity* (New York: Dover, 1952), 175–188. That translation can also be found in *The Collected Papers of Albert Einstein*, vol. 6, *The Berlin Years: Writings, 1914–1917 (English Translation Supplement)*, trans. Alfred Engel (Princeton, NJ: Princeton University Press, 1997). Available at https://einsteinpapers.press .princeton.edu/vol6-trans/433, 421–432.

3. "Uber die Hypothesen, welche der Geometrie zu Grunde liegen," Königliche Gesellschaft der Wissenschaften und dert Georg-Augustus-Universität (Göttingen), Mathematische Klasse (1867). English translation: B. Riemann, "On the Hypotheses which Lie at the Bases of Geometry," trans. William Kingdon Clifford, *Nature* 8, no. 183 (1873): 14–17, https://www.nature.com/articles /008014a0, and no. 184: 36–37, https://www.nature.com/articles/008036a0. Available at http://www.emis.de/classics/Riemann/.

4. Published as "Geometrie und Erfahrung," in *Stizungsberichte der Preussische Akademie der Wissenschaften*, vol. 1 (Berlin: Verlag von Julius Springer, 1921), 123–130. An English translation of the address is available here: "Geometry and Experience," *Math History*, University of St Andrews, April 2007, https://mathshistory.st -andrews.ac.uk/Extras/Einstein_geometry/.

5. Ernst Mach's work on gravity and the origin of inertia is collected in *Die Mechanik in ihrer Entwicklung, historisch-kritisch dargestellt* (Leipzig, Germany: Brockhaus, 1883). *The Science of Mechanics*, trans. T. McCormac (Chicago: Open Court Publishing, 1919).

6. In a letter to Bentley, Newton noted that if the distribution of matter in the universe occupied a finite volume within infinite space, matter near the outside of that volume would, by gravity, be attracted to matter from within, and as a result would fall to the center of the entire space to form a large spherical mass. Thus, the theory of universal gravitation implied that matter should be distributed in infinite space, in accordance with the cosmology of the Greek atomists, and in contradiction to the Stoic conception.

7. Einstein, "Cosmological Considerations," 431–432.

8. Immanuel Kant, *Critika der reinen Vernunft* (Germany, 1781). English translation *Critique of Pure Reason*, trans. Paul Guyer and Allen Wood (Cambridge, UK: Cambridge University Press, 1999), 157.

9. Einstein, "Geometry and Experience."

10. Einstein, "Geometry and Experience."

11. Einstein to Paul Ehrenfest, February 4, 1917.

12. Einstein, "Cosmological Considerations," 432.

13. W. de Sitter, "On Einstein's Theory of Gravitation and Its Astronomical Consequences," *Monthly Notices of the Royal Astronomical Society* 78 (1917): 3–28. In his 1933 journal article, H. P. Robertson attributed de Sitter's idea of the universe to his Dutch colleague Paul Ehrenfest.

14. He became its director in 1918 and remained so until his death. He was also president of the International Astronomical Union between 1925 and 1928.

15. V. M. Slipher, "Spectrographic Observations of Nebulae," *Popular Astronomy* 23 (1915): 21–24. The author reports fifteen measured radial velocities, eleven of which are positive.

16. The astronomical unit is the average distance between the Earth and the sun, or 150 million kilometers. Converted into light-years, the value given by de Sitter for the radius of space is therefore only 5 million light-years. The current estimated value is 9,000 times greater.

17. De Sitter, "On Einstein's Theory of Gravitation and Its Astronomical Consequences."

18. On the discussions between Einstein and de Sitter that followed, see Pierre Kerszberg, "The Einstein-de Sitter Controversy of 1916-1917 and the Rise of Relativistic Cosmology," in Don Howard and John Stachel, *Einstein and the History of General Relativity* (Boston: Birkhaüser, 1989).

4. ALEXANDER FRIEDMANN (1888–1925)

1. Paul Valéry, "On Poe's *Eureka*" [1921], in *Collected Works of Paul Valéry, Vol. 8: Leonardo, Poe, Mallarmé*, ed. Jackson Mathews, trans. Malcom Cowley and James R. Lawler (Princeton, NJ: Princeton University Press, 1972), 170.

2. The interested reader will find a comprehensive description of *Friedmann's* life and work in Eduard A. Tropp, Viktor Ya. Frenkel, and Artur D. Chernin, *Alexander Friedmann: The Man Who Made the Universe Expand* (Cambridge, UK: Cambridge University Press, 1993).

3. Harold Zirin, "Soviet Revolutions," review of *Alexander A. Friedmann: The Man Who Made the Universe Expand*, by E. A. Tropp, V. Ya. Frenkel, and A. D. Chernin, *Nature* 365 (October 28, 1993): 796.

4. V. K. Frederiks, "Obscij princip otnositel'nosti Ejnstejna" ["Observing the Principle of Einstein's Relativity"], *Uspekhi Fizicheskikh Nauk* [*Advances in Physical Sciences*], 2 (1922): 162–188.

5. V. K. Frederiks and A. A. Fridman, *Osnovy teorii otnositel'nosti, I: Tenzorial'noe ischislenie* [*Foundations of the Theory of Relativity, I: Tensor Calculus*] (St. Petersburg: Academia, 1924).

6. According to his former student George Gamow, Friedmann died of pneumonia contracted during his balloon flight. See G. Gamow, *My World Line: An Informal Autobiography* (New York: Viking Press, 1970).

5. ON THE CURVATURE OF SPACE (1922)

1. J. Thibaud, *Energie atomique et univers* (Lyons, France: Audin, 1945), 13. English translation of the quotation by Jean-Pierre Luminet.

2. A. Friedmann, "Über die Krümmung des Raumes," *Zeitschrift für Physik* 10 (1922): 377–386. The English translation quoted here is from Aleksandr Friedmann, "On the Curvature of Space," trans. Brian Doyle, in *A Source Book in Astronomy and Astrophysics, 1900–1975*, eds. Kenneth R. Lang and Owen Gingerich (Cambridge, MA: Harvard University Press, 1979), 838–843, https://archive.org/details

/sourcebookinastr0000unse/page/838/mode/2up?q=Doyle. The article was translated into Russian under the title "O krivizne prostranstva," *Zhurnal Russkago fiziko-khimicheskago obshchestva* 56, no. 1 (1924): 40–58, and in *Uspekhi Fizicheskikh Nauk* 80, no. 3 (1963): 439–446.

3. Georges Lemaître, "L'univers en expansion," *Annales de la Société Scientifique de Bruxelles* Ser. I A 53, 51 (1933).

4. Albert Einstein, *Zeitschrift für Physik* 11 (1922): 326. An English translation: *The Collected Papers of Albert Einstein, vol. 13, The Berlin Years: Writings and Correspondence January 1922–March 1923* (English Translation Supplement), trans. Ann M. Hentschel and Osik Moses (Princeton, NJ: Princeton University Press, 1998), document 340, https://einsteinpapers.press.princeton.edu/vol13-trans/301.

5. His objection is based on the equation $\partial \rho / \partial x_4 = 0$ instead of $\partial(\rho R^3) / \partial x4 = 0$, where ρ is the density, R the radius of the universe and x_4 the time variable.

6. Alexander Friedmann to Albert Einstein, December 6, 1922, in *The Collected Papers of Albert Einstein, vol. 13*, document 390, https://einsteinpapers.press .princeton.edu/vol13-trans/363.

7. V. Frenkel and A. A. Grib, "Einstein, Friedmann, Lemaître: Discovery of the Big Bang," *Proceedings of the 2nd Alexander Friedmann International Seminar on Gravitation and Cosmology*, eds. Yu Gnedin, A. Grib, and V. Mostepanenko (St. Petersburg: Friedmann Laboratory Publishing, 1994), 4, https://s3.cern.ch/inspire-prod -files-b/b94fee398939be224e068abe4309f32e.

8. Equivalent to the equation in Note 4 above.

9. Frenkel and Grib, "Einstein, Friedmann, Lemaître: Discovery of the Big Bang," 5.

10. Max Born to Albert Einstein, October 28, 1920, in *The Collected Papers of Albert Einstein*, vol. 10, *The Berlin Years: Correspondence, May–December 1920 (English Translation Supplement)*, trans. Ann M. Hentschel (Princeton, NJ: Princeton University Press, 1998), document 185, https://einsteinpapers.press.princeton.edu /vol10-trans/322.

11. Frenkel and Grib, "Einstein, Friedmann, Lemaître: Discovery of the Big Bang," 5–6.

12. Albert Einstein, *Zeitschrift für Physik* 16 (1923): 228. The English translation here is from *The Collected Papers of Albert Einstein, vol. 14, The Berlin Years: Writings and Correspondence April 1923–May 1925* (English Translation Supplement), trans. Ann M. Hentschel and Jennifer Nollar James (Princeton, NJ: Princeton University Press, 1998), document 51, https://einsteinpapers.press.princeton.edu/vol14 -trans/77.

13. J. Stachel, "Eddington and Einstein," in *The Prism of Science*, ed. E. Ulmann-Margarit (Dordrecht: D. Reidel, 1986).

14. This letter and those following are recorded by Frenkel and Grib, "Einstein, Friedmann, Lemaître: Discovery of the Big Bang," 7–8.

15. Emanuel von der Pahlen (1882–1952) was a German astronomer working at the Potsdam Observatory, best known for his work on stellar statistics. Doctor of Philosophy from the University of Göttingen, he had lived in St. Petersburg and had been Friedmann's assistant in Kiev. He left for Germany after the revolution of 1917. In 1924, he published a book entitled *The Infinity of Space and the Theory of Relativity*.

16. See K. Hentschel, "Erwin Finlay Freundlich and Testing Einstein's Theory of Relativity," *Archive for History of Exact Sciences* 47 (1994): 143–201.

6. THE WORLD AS SPACE AND TIME (1923)

1. English translation Alexander Friedmann, *The World as Space and Time*, trans. Vesselin Petkov (Montreal, Quebec, Canada: Minkowski Institute Press, 2016). French translation by A. Grib and the present author in Jean-Pierre Luminet, *Alexandre Friedmann, Georges Lemaître: Essais de Cosmologie* (Paris: Le Seuil, 1997).

2. *The World as Space and Time*, trans. V. Petkov, 2.

3. Quoted by Jean-Marc Lévy-Leblond, "L'arbre et la forêt: le mythe d'Einstein," in *L'esprit de sel* (Paris: Ed. du Seuil, 1984), 164.

4. Friedmann was familiar with at least two books on the theory of relativity written by philosophers and translated into Russian: Henri Bergson, *Duration and Simultaneity* (1922) and Ernst Cassirer, *Zur Einstein schen Relativitätstheorie* [*On Einstein's Theory of Relativity*] (Berlin, 1921), translated into Russian in 1922. Arthur Eddington's book, *Space, Time and Gravitation*, which Friedmann had read, as evidenced by the reference he gives at the end of his introduction, also contains philosophical considerations.

5. As we have seen, Einstein and Hilbert published almost simultaneously, in November 1915, the correct field equations for general relativity. Hilbert's article, "Die Grundlagen der Physik (Erste Mitteilung)," *Königliche Gesellschaft der Wissenschaft zu Göttingen. Mathematische-physikalische Klasse. Nachrichten* (1915): 395–407, contains important contributions to relativity that are absent from Einstein's work. See J. Mehra, *Einstein, Hilbert and the Theory of Gravitation* (Dordrecht, the Netherlands: D. Reidel, 1974).

6. English translation: David Hilbert, *Foundations of Geometry*, trans. E. J. Townsend (Sioux Falls, SD: Altus Classics, 2021).

7. Nicolas Bourbaki was a multi-talented author trained from 1933 onwards by mathematicians from the École Normale Supérieure de Paris. He took up modern mathematics in its foundations and built them on rigorous axiomatic bases in the spirit of Hilbert.

8. Ernest Nagel and James R. Newman, *Gödel's Proof* (New York: New York University Press, 2001).

9. B. Riemann, *Gesammelte mathematische Werke*, 2nd ed. (Leipzig, Germany: Teubner, 1892), 276.

10. Carl Friedrich Gauss, *Werke*, vol. 8 (Königlichen Gesellschaft der Wissenschaften zu Göttingen, 1900), 201.

11. George Boole, *The Mathematical Analysis of Logic* (Cambridge, UK: Macmillan, 1847).

12. Anecdote reported in Eduard A. Tropp, Viktor Ya. Frankel, and Artur D. Chernin, *Alexander Friedmann: The Man Who Made the Universe Expand* (Cambridge, UK: Cambridge University Press, 1993).

13. "From now on, space as such and time as such are condemned to vanish like ghosts, and only a kind of union of the two will be able to preserve an independent

reality." H. Minkowski, in "Die Grundgleichungen für die elektromagnetischen Vorgänge in bewegte Körpen," paper to the 80th Assembly of German Physicists, Köln (Königliche Gesselschaft der Wissenschaft zu Göttingen. Mathematische-physikalische Klasse, 1908). The corresponding article appeared posthumously in 1915, in "Das Relativitätsprinzip," *Annalen der Physik* 47 (1915): 927–938. English translation in H. A. Lorentz, A. Einstein, H. Minkowski, and H. Weyl, *The Principle of Relativity*, trans. W. Perrett and G. B. Jeffery (New York: Dover, 1923), https://archive.org/details/in.ernet.dli.2015.176699.

14. This point of view, still dominant, is not the only one; one can also consider general relativity as a non-linear field theory.

15. Hermann Weyl (1885–1955) was Hilbert's most gifted pupil. His book on relativity, *Raum, Zeit und Materie*, dates from 1918 and was republished many times. English translation: Hermann Weyl, *Space Time Matter*, trans. Henry L. Bose (London: Methuen, 1922), https://archive.org/details/in.ernet.dli.2015.43417/page/n5/mode/2up.

16. To treat all forces of Nature as manifestations of the structure of space-time is the outline of a unified theory, a problem still unsolved today.

17. Published by the Royal Academy of Belgium. See also *Elie Cartan-Albert Einstein: Letters on Absolute Parallelism, 1929–1932*, ed. Robert Debever (Princeton, NJ: Princeton University Press, 1979).

18. T. Kaluza, "Zum Unitätsproblem der Physik," *Sitzungsberichte Preussische Akademie der Wissenschaften* (1921): 966–972, and O. Klein, *Zeitschrift für Physik* 37 (1926): 895–906.

19. The analogy is from Andrey Grib, "Concepts of Modern Physics for Economists," St. Petersburg University of Economics and Finances, St. Petersburg, Russia.

20. For a popularized approach, see for example Brian Greene, *The Elegant Universe* (New York: Vintage, 2000).

21. Arthur S. Eddington, "A Generalization of Weyl's Theory of the Electromagnetic and Gravitational Fields," *Proceedings of the Royal Society* A 99 (1921): 104–122; and Eddington, *The Mathematical Theory of Relativity* (Cambridge, UK: Cambridge University Press, 1922), 91–97.

22. A. A. Friedmann and J. A. Schouten, "Über die Geometrie der halbsymmetrischen Übertragungen," *Math. Zeitschrift* 21 (1924): 3–4. The Dutch mathematician Jan Arnoldus Schouten (1883–1971) played an important role in the development of tensor calculus. Schouten applied his mathematical expertise to relativity in "Die direkte Analysis zur neueren Relativitätstheorie, Verhandelingen," *Koninklijke Akademie van Wetenschappen te Amsterdam*, vol. XII/6 (1918). See S. Golab, "The Scientific Work of Professor J. A. Schouten," *Demonstratio Mathematica* 4 (1972): 63–85.

23. Einstein did not venture to give numerical values in his 1917 cosmological article, but he had done so earlier in his popularizing work *Relativity: The Special and the General Theory*, published in German in 1916 and translated into English in 1920. The radius of curvature he indicated—about 10^8 light-years—was much too small and, correlatively, the average density of matter much too large (the currently accepted value of density is between one hundred and one thousand times lower). It is true that Einstein had only very incomplete observational data, to which he in

any case attributed little importance. It is curious to note that Einstein gave the same numerical values in a 1931 article, based however on a completely different model—the one precisely developed by Friedmann and Lemaître—taking into account cosmic expansion and the measured value of the rate of expansion. A. Einstein, "Zum kosmologischen Problem der allgemeinen Relativitätstheorie," *Preussische Akademie der Wissenschaften*, Sitzungsberichte (1931): 235–237. However, in order to arrive at the same figures as those he had put forward fifteen years earlier, Einstein made a miscalculation.

24. *The World as Space and Time*, trans. V. Petkov, 79.

25. On the modern point of view concerning a cosmic singularity—for example, whether it is an inevitable consequence of general relativity, and whether it took place at a single point or several, etc.—the reader may consult S. W. Hawking and G. F. R. Ellis, *The Large Scale Structure of Spacetime* (Cambridge, UK: Cambridge University Press, 1973), and, at a less technical level, S. Hawking and R. Penrose, *The Nature of Space and Time* (Princeton, NJ: Princeton University Press, 1996).

26. *The World as Space and Time*, trans. V. Petkov, 80.

27. Some conjectures on possible solutions can be found in Lee Smolin, *Three Roads to Quantum Gravity* (London: Weidenfeld & Nicolson, 2014), and Jean-Pierre Luminet, *L'écume de l'espace-temps* (France: Odile Jacob, 2020).

28. Andrey Grib, private communication.

29. When the Soviet scientific establishment finally embraced the Big Bang, it did so whole-heartedly, so much so that Soviet physicist Yacov B. Zeldovich declared in 1982, before the International Astronomical Union, that the Big Bang was "as certain as the fact that the Earth revolves around the Sun." He ignored the ironic remark of his compatriot Lev Landau that "cosmologists are often wrong, but never in doubt."

30. Andrey Grib, *Early Expanding Universe and Elementary Particles* (St. Petersburg, Russia: Friedmann Laboratory Publishing, 1995), 113.

31. *The World as Space and Time*, trans. V. Petkov, 80.

7. Space with Negative Curvature (1924)

1. A. Friedmann, "Über die Möglichkeit einer Welt mit konstanter negativer Krümmung des Raumes," *Zeitschrift für Physik* 21 (1924): 326–332. The article was translated into Russian in *Uspekhi Fizicheskikh Nauk* 93, no. 2 (1967): 280–287. The quotations here are from the English translation, "On the Possibility of a World with Constant Negative Curvature of Space," *General Relativity and Gravitation* 31 (December 1999), https://doi.org/10.1023/A:1026755309811. French translation by Jean-Pierre Luminet, in *Alexandre Friedmann, Georges Lemaître: Essais de Cosmologie* (Paris: Le Seuil, 1997).

2. Vladimir A. Fock was, along with George Gamow, Friedmann's most remarkable pupil. As he himself recalls in "The Researches of A. A. Fridman on the Einstein Theory of Gravitation," *Soviet Physics Uspekhi* 6, no. 4 (1964): 473–474, he translated Friedmann's first cosmological article into German, then pointed out to him the case of negatively curved spaces.

3. On the mathematical properties of spaces with constant curvature, see L. P. Eisenhart, *Riemannian Geometry* (Princeton, NJ: Princeton University Press, 1926), and J. Wolf, *Spaces of Constant Curvature*, 5th ed. (Wilmington, DE: Publish or Perish Inc., 1984).

4. H. P. Robertson and T. W. Noonan, *Relativity and Cosmology* (Philadelphia: W. B. Saunders, 1968). In relativistic cosmology, Howard P. Robertson was the first to combine the three possibilities (negative, zero, or positive constant curvature) into a single formal equation: "On the Foundations of Relativistic Cosmology," *Proceedings of the National Academy of Science* 15 (1929): 822–829, equation 10. This result was found again by Arthur G. Walker; see "On Milne's Theory of World Structure," *Proceedings of the London Mathematical Society* 42 (1936): 90–127, equation 90. The corresponding metric element is given by:

$$ds^2 = c^2\,dt^2 - R^2\,(t)\left[\frac{dr^2}{1 + Kr^2/4} + r^2\left(d\theta^2 + \sin^2\theta d\phi^2\right)\right]$$

where K is the constant of curvature. These "spatially homogeneous and isotropic" models of the universe have since been called "models of Friedmann—Lemaître—Robertson—Walker," abbreviated to FLRW.

5. Literally: "the fear of phantoms."

6. The surface obtained by "identifying" the diametrically opposed points of a sphere is the projective plane; Lemaître would be very interested in this surface.

7. Friedmann here corrects the erroneous assertion in his book *The Universe as Space and Time*, in which he suggested that a space with positive curvature was not necessarily finite (see Chapter 17).

8. Friedmann, "On the Possibility of a World with Constant Negative Curvature of Space."

8. Georges Lemaître (1894–1966)

1 The French poet and painter André Verdet (1913–2004), a friend of Jacques Prévert, Jean Cocteau, and Jean Giono, devoted several collections to the poetry of the stars and the universe. His book *L'obscur et L'ouvert* (Éditions Galilée, 1984) contains the long poem, "Hommages," of which I have only translated a very brief excerpt into English here.

2. Georges Lemaître, "La théorie de la relativité et l'expérience," *Revue des Questions Scientifiques, Quatrième série* 9 (1926): 346–374.

3. For a bibliography of Georges Lemaître, see A. Berger, "Bibliography of G. Lemaître," in *The Big Bang and Georges Lemaître: Proceedings of a Symposium in Honour of G. Lemaître*, ed. A. Berger (Dordrecht, the Netherlands: Springer, 1984), 399–407, https://link.springer.com/chapter/10.1007/978-94-009-6487-7_32.

4. For this biographical summary, I closely follow the excellent summary of Odon Godart, "Monseigneur Lemaître, sa vie, son œuvre," *Revue des Questions Scientifique* (1984): 155–182. For a more complete biography, see D. Lambert, *Un atome d'univers: La vie et l'œuvre de Georges Lemaître* (Bruxelles: Lessius, 2000). English translation: L. Ampleman, *The Atom of the Universe: The Life and Work of Georges Lemaître* (Krakow, Poland: Copernicus Center Press, 2015).

5. Interview with *The New York Times Magazine*, February 19, 1933.

6. Recently translated as *Learning the Physics of Einstein with Georges Lemaître: Before the Big Bang Theory*, eds. Jan Govaerts and J. F. Stoffel, trans. Christine Leroy and Stephen N. Lyle (Cham, Switzerland: Springer, 2019).

7. Arthur S. Eddington, *The Mathematical Theory of Relativity* (Cambridge, UK: Cambridge University Press, 1922).

8. A. V. Douglas, "Forty Minutes with Einstein," *Journal of the Royal Astronomical Society of Canada*, 50 (1956): 99.

9. For the question of Eddington's influence on Lemaître, see Dominique Lambert, *The Atom of the Universe*, trans. Luc Ampleman (Krakow, Poland: Copernicus Center Press, 2015).

10. In Alice Vibert Douglas, *The Life of Arthur Stanley Eddington* (Edinburgh, Scotland: Thomas Nelson, 1956), 111.

11. See Donald E. Osterbrock's reflections on this, quoted in William Sheehan and Christopher J. Conselice, *Galactic Encounters: Our Majestic and Evolving Star-System from the Big Bang to Time's End* (New York: Springer 2016), 174.

12. After the astronomer's death in 1953, his wife, Grace Hubble, gave the following romanticized description of him: "He looked an Olympian, tall, strong and beautiful, with the shoulders of the Hermes of Praxiteles, and the benign serenity." Quoted in Donald E. Osterbrock, Ronald S. Brashear, and Joel A. Gwinn, "Self-Made Cosmologist: The Education of Edwin Hubble," ASP Conference Series 10, *Evolution of the Universe of Galaxies; Proceedings of the Edwin Hubble Centennial Symposium*, ed. Richard G. Kron (San Francisco: ASP): 13, https://articles.adsabs.harvard.edu//full/1990ASPC...10....1O/0000013.000.html.

13. Georges H. J. E. Lemaître, "The Gravitational Field in a Fluid Sphere of Uniform Invariant Density according to the Theory of Relativity," (PhD diss., MIT, 1927), https://dspace.mit.edu/handle/1721.1/10753. Georgy Abramovich Grinberg, a student of Friedmann, had defended a thesis on the same subject in 1924 (see *Journal of the Russian Physical Chemical Society* 56 (1925): 368, which was ignored because it was written in Russian.

14. A. Krasinski, *Inhomogeneous Cosmological Model* (Cambridge, UK: Cambridge University Press, 1997).

15. For these and other details about Lemaître, see D. Lambert, "A Universe from an Atom," Il Nuovo Saggiatore 32, no. 3–4 (2106): 55–66.

16. Published posthumously: Georges Lemaître, *Une paire de Molière(s)* (Brussels: Samsa Editions, 2013).

17. Lemaître supported associations welcoming Chinese students in Belgium. During his seminary time he learned Chinese thanks to the presence of a Chinese seminarian.

9. Galaxy Recession and Cosmic Expansion (1927–1931)

1. The poem "Hommages," of which this quotation is only a brief excerpt, is from Verdet's *L'obscur et L'ouvert* (Éditions Galilée, 1984).

2. Sir William Huggins and Lady Margaret Huggins, *The Scientific Papers of Sir William Huggins* (London: Wesley, 1909).

3. On the history of the Great Debate, see Robert Smith, *The Expanding Universe: Astronomy's "Great Debate," 1900–1931* (Cambridge, UK: Cambridge University Press, 1982).

4. "NGC 6822, a Remote Stellar System," *Astrophysical Journal* 62 (1925): 409–433.

5. Hubble believed that the Magellanic Clouds, later recognized as the two closest galaxies, belonged to our Milky Way.

6. "A Spiral Nebula as a Stellar System: Messier 33," *Astrophysical Journal* 63 (1926): 236.

7. "A Spiral Nebula as a Stellar System, Messier 31," *Astrophysical Journal* 69 (1929): 103. It should be noted in passing that Messier 31 is traditionally presented as the first Hubble-certified galaxy. It is true that the photometric beauty of this nebula is much more impressive than that of the two previous ones and thus may have made a greater impression. And many authors simply repeat what they have read elsewhere without going back to the original sources.

8. See for example H. S. Kragh and D. Lambert, "The Context of Discovery: Lemaître and the Origin of the Primeval-Atom Universe," *Annals of Science* 64 (2007): 445–470.

9. H. Weyl, *Zeitschrift für Physik* 24 (1923): 230.

10. C. Wirtz, "De Sitters Kosmologie und die Radialbewegungen der Spiralnebel," *Astronomische Nachrichten* 222, no. 21 (1924); L. Silberstein, "The Curvature of de Sitter's Space-Time Derived from Globular Clusters," *Monthly Notices of the Royal Astronomical Society* 84 (1924): 363; K. Lundmark, "The Motions and the Distances of Spiral Nebulae," *Monthly Notices of the Royal Astronomical Society* 85 (1925): 865.

11. Georges Lemaître, "Note on de Sitter's Universe," *The Physical Review* 25 (1925): 903; "Note on de Sitter's Universe," *Journal of Mathematics and Physics* 4 (1925): 189–192.

12. See for example Andrei Linde, *Particle Physics and Inflationary Cosmology* (Chur, Switzerland: Harwood, 1990), https://arxiv.org/abs/hep-th/0503203.

13. An earlier version of the rest of this chapter first appeared as Jean-Pierre Luminet, "Editorial Note to Georges Lemaître, A Homogenous Universe of Constant Mass and Increasing Radius Accounting for the Radial Velocity of Extra-Galactic Nebulae," *General Relativity and Gravitation* 46 (June 13, 2013): 1619–1633, https://link.springer.com/article/10.1007/s10714-013-1547-4.

14. See Ken Freeman, "Slipher and the Nature of the Nebulae," in *Origins of the Expanding Universe: 1912–1932, ASP Conference Series* 471 (2013), https://arxiv.org/pdf/1301.7509.pdf, and references therein.

15. Quoted in Freeman, "Slipher and the Nature of the Nebulae," 4.

16. V. M. Slipher, "Nebulae," *Proceedings of the American Philosophical Society* 56, no. 5 (1917): 409, https://www.jstor.org/stable/984028?seq=1.

17. Vesto Melvin Slipher, "Dreyer Nebula no. 584 Inconceivably Distant," *New York Times*, January 19, 1921, 61, https://www.nytimes.com/1921/01/19/archives/dreyer-nebula-no-584-inconceivably-distant-dr-slipher-says-the.html.

18. On the modest personality of Slipher, see John A. Peacock, "Slipher, Galaxies and Cosmological Velocity Fields," in *Origins of the Expanding Universe: 1912–1932, ASP Conference Series* 471 (2013). Available at Cornell University ArXiv (2013), https://arxiv.org/abs/1301.7286.

19. Arthur Eddington, *The Mathematical Theory of Relativity* (Cambridge, UK: Cambridge University Press, 1922), 273.

20. English translation of a letter of January 21, 1945, to Ferdinand Gonseth, Archives Lemaître, Louvain-la-Neuve.

21. M. Lachièze-Rey and Jean-Pierre Luminet, *Figures du Ciel* (Paris: Seuil/BnF, 1998) 155. English translation: *Celestial Treasury* (Cambridge, UK: Cambridge University Press, 2001).

22. Odon Godart, "Monseigneur Lemaître, sa vie, son œuvre," *Revue des Questions Scientifique* 155 (1984): 155–182.

23. *Revue des Questions Scientifiques* 15 (1929): 9–36.

24. G. Strömberg, "Analysis of Radial Velocities of Globular Clusters and Non-Galactic Nebulae," *Astrophysical Journal* 61 (1925): 353. Strömberg himself relied on redshifts measured by Slipher and included some globular clusters in addition to spiral nebulae.

25. E. Hubble, "A Relation between Distance and Radial Velocity among Extra-Galactic Nebulae," *Contributions from the Mount Wilson Observatory*, Carnegie Institution of Washington 310 (1927): 1; J. Hopmann, "Photometric Untersuchungen von Nebelecken," *Astronomische Nachrichten* 214 (1921): 425.

26. The paper was reprinted later in 1927 in volume 4 of *Publications du Laboratoire d'Astronomie et de Géodésie de l'Université de Louvain*, still less suited for widespread dissemination!

27. D. Lambert, "A propos de la controverse Hubble-Lemaître," *Pour la Science* 412 (February 2012): 78–81.

28. Georges Lemaître, "Rencontres avec A. Einstein," *Revue des Questions Scientifiques*, 70e année, t. 129, 5e série, t. 19, no. 1 (January 20, 1958): 129–132.

29. André Deprit, notes added to O. Godart, "Monseigneur Lemaître, sa vie, son œuvre." English translation by Jean-Pierre Luminet.

30. Dominique Lambert, "Religious Interferences at the Origin of Cosmology? The Case of Georges Lemaître," *Forum* 4 (2018): 149–168, https://forum-phil.pusc.it/sites/default/files/pdf/forum-v04-a10.pdf.

31. Baruch Spinoza, *Ethics* [1677] II, note to Proposition VII, https://en.wikisource.org/wiki/Ethics_(Spinoza)/Part_2.

32. H. P. Robertson, "On Relativistic Cosmology," *Philosophical Magazine, Series Seven* 5 (1928): 835.

33. Robertson did not calculate this proportionality factor, but the figure can be found in Hilmar W. Duerbeck and Waltraut C. Seitter, "In Hubble's Shadow: Early Research on the Expansion of the Universe," in *One Hundred Years of Observational Astronomy and Astrophysics*, eds. C. Sterken and J. B. Hearnshaw (Brussels: C. Sterken, 2001), Chapter 15, https://www.researchgate.net/publication/241349632_In_Hubble's_shadow_early_research_on_the_expansion_of_the_universe.

34. H. P. Robertson, "On the Foundations of Relativistic Cosmology," *Proceedings of the National Academy of Sciences* 15, no. 11 (1929): 822–829, https://doi.org/10.1073/pnas.15.11.822.

35. Edwin Hubble, "A Relation between Distance and Radial Velocity among Extra-Galactic Nebulae," *Proceedings of the National Academy of Sciences* 15, no. 3 (March 15, 1929): 168.

36. Hubble, "A Relation between Distance and Radial Velocity among Extra-Galactic Nebulae," 173.

37. This work is not really a popularizing text and is not very engaging on the literary level.

38. Edwin Hubble, *The Realm of the Nebulae* (New Haven, CT: Yale University Press, 1936); page references are to the 1958 Dover reprint edition.

39. G. E. Christianson, *Edwin Hubble: Mariner of the Nebulae* (Chicago, IL: University of Chicago Press, 1996): 201.

40. See for example S. van den Bergh, "Discovery of the Expansion of the Universe," *Journal of the Royal Astronomical Society of Canada* (2011), https://arxiv.org/abs /1108.0709.

41. Quoted in David L. Block, "A Hubble Eclipse: Lemaître and Censorship," Cornell University ArXiv (2011), https://arxiv.org/abs/1106.3928v1, with a slightly revised version later appearing as "Georges Lemaître and Stigler's Law of Eponymy," in *Georges Lemaître: Life, Science and Legacy. Astrophysics and Space Science Library 395*, eds. R. Holder and S. Mitton (Berlin: Springer, 2012), https://arxiv.org/abs /1106.3928v3.

42. Richard C. Tolman, "On the Possible Line Elements for the Universe," *Proceedings of the National Academy of Sciences* 15 (1929): 297, https://www.pnas.org/doi/abs /10.1073/pnas.15.4.297.

43. Richard C. Tolman, "The Effect of the Annihilation of Matter on the Wave-Length of Light from the Nebulae," *Proceedings of the National Academy of Sciences* 16 (1930): 320, https://www.pnas.org/doi/abs/10.1073/pnas.16.4.320.

44. Arthur S. Eddington, "Remarks at the Meeting of the Royal Astronomical Society," *The Observatory* 53 (1930): 39–40.

45. From a copy kept at the Archives Lemaître of Louvain-la-Neuve, quoted in D. Lambert, "A propos de la controverse Hubble-Lemaître," *Pour la Science* 412 (February 2012): 78–81.

46. Quoted in H. Kragh, *Cosmology and Controversy* (Princeton, NJ: Princeton University Press, 1996), Chapter 2.

47. Quoted in H. Kragh, *Cosmology and Controversy*.

48. Reported in P. J. E. Peebles, *Principles of Physical Cosmology* (Princeton, NJ: Princeton University Press, 1993), 80.

49. Originally written in French, this letter and the two following ones, found in the Archives Lemaître (Université de Louvain), were for the first time displayed in Jean-Pierre Luminet, *Alexandre Friedmann, Georges Lemaître: Essais de Cosmologie* (Paris: Le Seuil, 1997). English translation by the present author.

50. W. De Sitter, "On the Distances and Radial Velocities of Extra-galactic Nebulae, and the Explanation of the Latter by the Relativity Theory of Inertia," *Proceedings of the National Academy of Sciences* 16, no. 7 (1930): 474–488.

51. Arthur S. Eddington, *The Observatory* 53 (1930): 162–164.

52. Arthur S. Eddington, "On the Instability of Einstein's Spherical World," *Monthly Notices of the Royal Astronomical Society* 90 (1930): 668–678.

53. Georges Lemaître, "A Homogeneous Universe of Constant Mass and Increasing Radius Accounting for the Radial Velocity of Extra-Galactic Nebulae," *Monthly Notices of the Royal Astronomical Society* 41 (1931): 483–490.

54. Jean-Pierre Luminet, "Editorial Note to 'The Beginning of the World from the Point of View of Quantum Theory,'" *Journal of General Relativity and Gravitation* 43, no. 10 (2011): 2911–2928, https://arxiv.org/abs/1105.6271.

55. S. L. Jaki, *Science and Creation* (Edinburgh, Scotland: Scottish Academic Press, 1974); R. W. Smith, *The Expanding Universe, Astronomy's "Great Debate" 1900–1931* (Cambridge, UK: Cambridge University Press, 1982); O. Godart and M. Heller, *Cosmology of Lemaître* (Tucson, AZ: Pachart Pub. House, 1985); Jean-Pierre Luminet, *Alexandre Friedmann, Georges Lemaître: Essais de Cosmologie*, coll. "Sources du Savoir" (Paris: Le Seuil, 1997); D. Lambert, *Un atome d'univers: La vie et l'œuvre de Georges Lemaître* (Bruxelles: Lessius, 2000). English translation: L. Ampleman, *The Atom of the Universe: The Life and Work of Georges Lemaître* (Krakow, Poland: Copernicus Center Press, 2015); Helge Kragh and Robert W. Smith, "Who Discovered the Expanding Universe?," *History of Science* 41, no. 2 (2003): 141; J. Farrell, *The Day Without Yesterday: Lemaître, Einstein, and the Birth of Modern Cosmology* (New York: Thunders Mouth Press, 2005); H. Nussbaumer and L. Bieri, *Discovering the Expanding Universe* (Cambridge, UK: Cambridge University Press, 2009).

56. Paul Couderc, *L'expansion de l'Univers* (Paris: Presses Universitaires de France, 1950).

57. D. Lambert, "Georges Lemaître: Repères biographiques." *Revue des Questions Scientifiques* 183, no. 4 (2012): 337–398.

58. P. J. E. Peebles, *Principles of Physical Cosmology* (Princeton, NJ: Princeton University Press, 1993), 80; H. Kragh, *Cosmology and Controversy* (Princeton, NJ: Princeton University Press, 1996), Chapter 2; Luminet, *Alexandre Friedmann, Georges Lemaître*.

59. Sidney van den Bergh, "The Curious Case of Lemaître's Equation No. 24," *Journal of the Royal Astronomical Society of Canada* 105 (2011): 151–152 https://arxiv.org/abs/1106.1195; Eugenie Samuel Reich, "Edwin Hubble in Translation Trouble," *Nature* (2011), https://doi.org/10.1038/news.2011.385.

60. Block, "A Hubble Eclipse: Lemaître and Censorship."

61. Mario Livio, "Mystery of the Missing Text Solved," *Nature* 479 (2011): 171–173, https://www.nature.com/articles/479171a.

62. The detailed list of all the discrepancies between the French original of 1927 and the English translation of 1931 has been analyzed in Jean-Pierre Luminet, "Editorial Note to 'A Homogenous Universe of Constant Mass and Increasing Radius Accounting for the Radial Velocity of Extra-Galactic Nebulae' by Georges Lemaître (1927)," *General Relativity and Gravitation* 45 (2013): 1619–1646, https://link.springer.com/article/10.1007/s10714-013-1547-4.

63. Georges Lemaître, "Compte-rendu du livre 'L'univers en expansion' de Paul Couderc," *Annales d'Astrophysique* 13, no. 3 (1950): 344–345.

64. The top graph, based on Lemaître's data, reconstructed in Hilmar W. Duerbeck and Waltraut C. Seitter, "In Hubble's Shadow: Early Research on the Expansion of the Universe," in *One Hundred Years of Observational Astronomy and Astrophysics*, eds. C. Sterken and J. B. Hearnshaw (Brussels: C. Sterken, 2001), Chapter 15, https://www.researchgate.net/publication/241349632_In_Hubble's_shadow_early_research_on_the_expansion_of_the_universe. The bottom graph is from Edwin Hubble, "A Relation between Distance and Radial Velocity among Extra-galactic Nebulae, " *PNAS* 15, no. 3 (April 25, 1929): 168–173, https://www.pnas.org/doi/full/10.1073/pnas.15.3.168.

65. Freeman, "Slipher and the Nature of the Nebulae," 68.

66. Mario Livio, "Mystery of the Missing Text Solved," *Nature* 479 (2011), 173, https://doi.org/10.1038/479171a.

67. Notes from Georges Lemaître's course on the "Theory of Relativity" (1960–1961) written by J.-P. Antoine, Louvain, unpublished, 60–63.

68. Paul Couderc, *L'expansion de l'univers* (Paris: Presses Universitaires de France, 1950).

69. Georges Lemaître, "L'expansion de l'univers, Bibliographie," *Annales d'Astrophysique* 13 (1950): 344.

70. David. L. Block, "Georges Lemaître and Stigler's Law of Eponymy," (2011), https://arxiv.org/pdf/1106.3928.pdf.

10. The Quantum Birth of the Universe (1931)

1. This chapter relies heavily on Jean-Pierre Luminet, "Editorial Note to: Georges Lemaître, the Beginning of the World from the Point of View of Quantum Theory," *General Relativity and Gravitation* 43 (2011): 2911–2928, https://link.springer.com/article/10.1007/s10714-011-1213-7.

2. Abbé G. Lemaître, "A Homogenous Universe of Constant Mass and Increasing Radius," *Monthly Notices of the Royal Astronomical Society* 91 (March 1931) : 483–490.

3. Abbé G. Lemaître, "The Expanding Universe," *Monthly Notices of the Royal Astronomical Society* 91 (March 1931) : 490–501, https://adsabs.harvard.edu/full/1931MNRAS..91..490L. This article is not to be confused with Georges Lemaître, "L'Univers en expansion," *Annales de la Société Scientifique de Bruxelles*, série A, t. III (1933): 51-85; for the English translation of the latter essay, see "The Expanding Universe," trans. M. A. H. MacCallum, *General Relativity and Gravitation* 29, no. 5 (1997): 641–680, http://dx.doi.org/10.1023/A:1018855621348.

4. Georges Lemaître, "L'expansion de l'espace," *Revue des Questions Scientifiques* 17 (1931), 391–440. An English translation was later published in Georges Lemaître, *The Primeval Atom: An Essay on Cosmogony*, trans. Betty H. and Serge A. Korff (Canada: D. Van Nostrand Co., 1950), https://archive.org/details/primevalatom0000unse/page/n5/mode/2up.

5. Lemaître isolates Eddington's quotation from its context, which may lend itself to an incorrect interpretation of the British scholar's attitude. Eddington refers to a conclusion regarded as unambiguously affirmative of a literal reading of the creation accounts found in the Bible—in particular, the idea that God created the Universe out of nothing a finite time ago. Eddington was a Quaker and as such was wary of dogmatic certainties and sought to avoid imposing an authoritative interpretation on the Bible. His views on religion and science were expressed in several publications, including "The Nature of the Physical World" (1927) and his Swarthmore lecture of 1929, "Science and the Unseen World." A study of the influence of his Quaker beliefs on his approach to science can be found in A. H. Batten, "A Most Rare Vision—Eddington's Thinking on the Relation between Science and Religion," *Quarterly Journal of the Royal Astronomical Society*, 35, no. 3 (Sept. 1994), 249.

6. Georges Lemaître, "The Beginning of the World from the Point of View of Quantum Theory," *Nature* 127 (May 9, 1931): 706, https://www.nature.com/articles/127706b0.

7. Arthur S. Eddington, "The End of the World from the Standpoint of Mathematical Physics," *Nature* 127 (March 21, 1931): 447–453, https://doi.org/10.1038 /127447a0. Eddington's lecture was also transcribed in the *Mathematical Gazette* 15, no. 212 (March 1931): 316–324, https://www.jstor.org/stable/3606671.

8. Eddington, "The End of the World from the Standpoint of Mathematical Physics," *Nature*: 450; *Mathematical Gazette*: 319.

9. Lemaître was not the first to suggest a connection between cosmology and quantum theory. As early as 1925, Cornelius Lanczos ("Über eine zeitlich periodische Welt und eine neue Behandlung des Problems der Atherstrahlung," *Zeitschrift für Physik* 32 (1925): 56–80), introduced quantum mechanics in a cosmological model, concluding that "The solution of the quantum secrets is hidden in the spatial and temporal closedness of the world." Quoted in Helge Kragh and Dominique Lambert, "The Context of Discovery: Lemaître and the Origin of the Primeval-Atom Universe," *Annals of Science* 64, no. 4 (October 2007): n37.

10. N. Bohr, "The Use of the Concepts of Space and Time in Atomic Theory," *Nature* 127 (1931): 43.

11. Helge S. Kragh and Dominique Lambert, "The Context of Discovery: Lemaître and the Origin of the Primeval-Atom Universe," *Annals of Science* 64, no. 4 (2007): 445–470.

12. Dominique Lambert, "A Universe from an Atom," *Il Nuovo Saggiatore* 32, no. 3–4 (2016): 55–66, https://www.ilnuovosaggiatore.sif.it/article/34.

13. Dominique Lambert, "Religious Interferences at the Origin of Cosmology? The Case of Georges Lemaître," *Forum* 4 (2018): 149–168, https://forum-phil.pusc.it /sites/default/files/pdf/forum-v04-a10.pdf. The relations between science and religious faith in Lemaître's thought have also been analyzed in O. Godart, "Contributions of Lemaître to General Relativity (1922–1934)," in *Studies in the History of General Relativity*, eds. A. J. Kox and Jean Eisenstaedt (Boston: Birkhäuser, 1992); O. Godart and M. Heller, "Les relations entre la science et la foi chez Georges Lemaître," *Commentarii, Pontifical Academy of Sciences* 3, no. 121: 1–12, https://www.pas.va/en/publications/commentarii/commentarii-iii-21.html; D. Lambert, "Mgr. Georges Lemaître et les 'Amis de Jésus,'" *Revue Théologique de Louvain* 27 (1996): 309–343; and Dominique Lambert, "Monseigneur Georges Lemaître et le débat entre la cosmologie et la foi," *Revue Théologique de Louvain* 28, no. 2 (1997): 227–243. Lemaître himself expressed himself on the question in "La culture catholique et les sciences positives," *Actes du VIe congrès catholique de Malines*, t. V, 65–70.

14. Today, some physicists and astronomers—mainly in the Anglo-Saxon world— routinely invoke the name of God to describe discoveries. In 1992 UC Berkeley astronomer George Smoot (winner of the Nobel Prize in 2006) compared the first glimpse of the earliest structures in the universe—anisotropies in the cosmic background radiation left over from the Big Bang—to "seeing the face of God." Quoted in "Finders of Big Bang Afterglow Win Nobel Prize," *New Scientist*, October 4, 2006, https://www.newscientist.com/article/mg19225723-000-finders -of-big-bang-afterglow-win-nobel-prize/. In 2005 Nobel Laureate Charles Townes commented, "Intelligent design, as one sees it from a scientific point of view, seems to be quite real. This is a very special universe: it's remarkable that it came out just this way. If the laws of physics weren't just the way they are, we couldn't be here at

all. The sun couldn't be there, the laws of gravity and nuclear laws and magnetic theory, quantum mechanics, and so on have to be just the way they are for us to be here." Quoted in Bonnie Azab Powell, "'Explore as Much as We Can': Nobel Prize Winner Charles Townes on Evolution, Intelligent Design, and the Meaning of Life," *UC Berkeley News*, June 17, 2005, https://newsarchive.berkeley.edu/news /media/releases/2005/06/17_townes.shtml. For several other examples of leading physicists and astronomers pointing to evidence in physics and cosmology supportive of intelligent design, see Jonathan Witt, "Does George Smoot, Nobel Laureate, See Evidence of Design in the Cosmos?" *Evolution News & Science Today*, February 2, 2007, https://evolutionnews.org/2007/02/does_george_smoot_nobel_laurea/.

15. Georges Lemaître, quoted in Duncan Aikman, "Lemaître Follows Two Paths to Truth," *New York Times*, February 19, 1933, https://inters.org/files/lemaitre_two _paths_truth_nyt1933.pdf.

16. Lambert, "Religious Interferences." See also Joseph R. Laracy, *The Faith and Reason of Father Georges Lemaître* (San Francisco, CA: Ignatius Press, 2009): 50–59.

17. Fernand Van Steenberghen, *Dieu Caché: Comment Savons-Nous Que Dieu Existe?* (Paris: Louvain,1960), 130–131. English translation by the present author.

18. Elio Gentili and Ivan Tagliaferri, *Scienza e fede: i protagonisti: sacerdoti e religiosi scienziati* (Rome: Instituto Geografico de Agostini, 1989), 287. Quoted in Joseph Laracy, "The Faith and Reason of Father Georges Lemaître," https://www.catholic culture.org/culture/library/view.cfm?recnum=8847.

19. Georges Lemaître, *The Expanding Universe: Lemaître's Unknown Manuscript*, introduction by O. Godart and M. Heller (Tucson, AZ: Pachart Publishing House, 1985): 47.

11. The Expansion of Space (1931)

1. "Contributions to a British Association Discussion on the Evolution of the Universe," *Supplement to Nature* 128 (October 24, 1931), https://www.nature.com /nature/volumes/128/issues/3234. Scroll down to the Research Article section to see individual contributions.

2. Georges Lemaître, "The Expanding Universe," *Monthly Notices of the Royal Astronomical Society* 41 (1931): 491–501.

3. Georges Lemaître, Untitled contribution to session on "The Question of the Relation of the Physical Universe to Life and Mind" at the British Association for the Advancement of Science, 29 September 1941, published in *Nature* 128 (October 24, 1931): 705, https://www.nature.com/articles/128704a0.

4. Lemaître, contribution to "The Question of the Relation of the Physical Universe to Life and Mind," 706.

5. Lemaître, contribution to "The Question of the Relation of the Physical Universe to Life and Mind," 705.

6. In André Deprit's notes added to Odon Godart's article, "Monseigneur Lemaître, sa vie, son œuvre," *Revue des Questions Scientifique* 155 (1984): 155–182.

7. Georges Lemaître, *L'Hypothèse de l'atome primitif. Essai de cosmogonie* (Neuchâtel, Switzerland), Editions du Griffon, and Brussels, Editions Hermès, 1946. English translation: Georges Lemaître, *The Primeval Atom: An Essay on Cosmogony*, trans.

Betty H. and Serge A. Korff (Canada: D. Van Nostrand Co., 1950), https://archive
.org/details/primevalatom0000unse/page/n5/mode/2up.

8. Lemaître, *The Primeval Atom*, 56.

9. English translation: Immanuel Kant, *Universal Natural History and Theory of the Heavens* [1755], trans. Ian Johnston (Vancouver, Canada: Vancouver Island University, 1998), https://johnstoniatexts.x10host.com/kant/kant2e.htm.

10. Lemaître, *The Primeval Atom*, 56.

11. Lemaître, *The Primeval Atom*, 56.

12. E. P. Hubble, "NGC 6822, A Remote Stellar System," *Astrophysical Journal* 62 (1925): 409–433; Hubble, "Extra-Galactic Nebulae," *Astrophysical Journal* 64 (1926): 321.

13. A. Einstein, *Theory of Relativity: Its Formal Content and Present Problems* (Oxford, UK: Oxford University Press, 1931).

14. Lemaître, *The Primeval Atom*, 57.

15. Lemaître anticipates here the idea that the fundamental equations of cosmic dynamics can be obtained using simple Newtonian considerations. This approach, baptized "Newtonian Cosmology," would be presented in 1934 by the British astrophysicists Edward Milne and William McCrea; see E. Milne, "A Newtonian Expanding Universe," *Quarterly Journal of Mathematics* 5 (1934): 64; W. McCrea and E. Milne, "Newtonian Universes and the Curvature Of Space," *Quarterly Journal of Mathematics* 5 (1934): 73.

16. Lemaître, *The Primeval Atom*, 60–61.

17. Lemaître, *The Primeval Atom*, 63.

18. See for example Frank J. Tipler, "Rigorous Newtonian Cosmology," *American Journal of Physics* 64 (October 1996): 1311.

19. Lemaître, *The Primeval Atom*, 64.

20. Lemaître, *The Primeval Atom*, 64.

21. Albert Einstein, "Kosmologische Betrachtungen zur allgemeinen Relativitäts-theorie," in *Preussische Akademie der Wissenschaften, Sitzungsberichte* (Berlin, 1917), 142–152. See also Einstein, "Cosmological Considerations in the General Theory of Relativity," trans. W. Perrett and G. B. Jeffery, in H. A. Lorentz et al., *The Principle of Relativity* (New York: Dover, 1952), reprinted in *The Collected Papers of Albert Einstein*, vol. 6, *The Berlin Years: Writings, 1914–1917 (English Translation Supplement)*, trans. Alfred Engel (Princeton, NJ: Princeton University Press, 1997), document 43, https://einsteinpapers.press.princeton.edu/vol6-trans/433, 421–432.

22. Lemaître, *The Primeval Atom*, 65.

23. Lemaître, *The Primeval Atom*, 68.

24. Lemaître, *The Primeval Atom*, 68–69.

25. Walter Baade, "A Revision of the Extra-Galactic Distance Scale," *Transactions of the International Astronomical Union* 8 (1952): 397.

26. Lemaître, *The Primeval Atom*, 69.

27. Lemaître, *The Primeval Atom*, 69.

28. Lemaître, *The Primeval Atom*, 70–71.

29. Lemaître, *The Primeval Atom*, 71.

30. Lemaître, *The Primeval Atom*, 71.

31. Lemaître, *The Primeval Atom*, 71–72.

32. Radioactivity, i.e., the spontaneous emission of radiation by matter, was discovered in 1896 by Henri Becquerel (1852–1908). In 1903, Becquerel had shared the Nobel Prize in Physics with Pierre Curie (1859–1906) and Marie Curie (1867–1934), the very term "radioactivity" having been proposed by the latter.

33. Lemaître, *The Primeval Atom*, 72.

34. Lemaître, *The Primeval Atom*, 72.

35. Lemaître, *The Primeval Atom*, 75.

36. Lemaître, *The Primeval Atom*, 78.

37. Here Lemaître describes his model that includes a cosmological constant, a model which has three distinct phases: two periods of rapid expansion separated by a period of slowdown. See Figure 11.1.

38. Lemaître, *The Primeval Atom*, 78–79.

39. Lemaître, *The Primeval Atom*, 79–80.

40. Frank Dyson, "Time Without End: Physics and Biology in an Open Universe," *Reviews of Modern Physics* 51 (1979): 447–460. See also Jean-Pierre Luminet, *Le Destin de l'Univers* (Paris: Fayard, 2006).

41. Lemaître, *The Primeval Atom*, 79.

42. Lemaître, *The Primeval Atom*, 79. Here I have provided my own translation.

43. D. H. Menzel, "Blast of Giant Atom Created Our Universe," *Popular Science Monthly*, December 1932, 28–30.

44. Pascual Jordan, *Die Physik des 20 Jahrhunderts* (Braunschweig, Germany,1936); English translation *Physics of the Twentieth Century* (New York: Philosophical Library, 1944), https://archive.org/details/physicsofthe20th000928mbp.

45. A. Einstein, "Zum kosmologischen Problem der allgemeinen Relativitätstheorie," *Sitzungberichte der Preussischen Akademie der Wissenschaften* (1931), 235–237.

46. In Odon Godart, "Monseigneur Lemaître, sa vie, son œuvre," *Revue des Questions Scientifique* (1984).

12. Cosmological Regression (1932)

1. Georges Lemaître, *The Primeval Atom: An Essay on Cosmogony*, trans. Betty H. and Serge A. Korff (Canada: D. Van Nostrand Co., 1950), 133, https://archive.org /details/primevalatom0000unse/page/n5/mode/2up.

2. A. Einstein, "Zum kosmologischen Problem der allgemeinen Relativitätstheorie," *Preussische Akademie der Wissenschaften, Sitzungsberichte* (1931): 235–237. Available in English translation in C. O'Raifeartaigh and B. McCann, "Einstein's Cosmic Model of 1931 Revisited; An Analysis and Translation of a Forgotten Model of the Universe," *European Physical Journal (H)* 39, no. 1: 63–85, https://arxiv.org/abs /1312.2192.

3. This little-known article was written in late 1932 and published in French in 1933. A. Einstein, "*Sur la Structure Cosmologique de l'Espace*," trans. Maurice Solovine, in *Les Fondaments de la Théorie de la Relativité Générale* (Paris: Hermann et Cie,

1933). The earliest English translation and an explanation of its history are given by Cormac O'Raifeartaigh et al., "Einstein's Cosmology Review of 1933: A New Perspective on the de Sitter Model of the Cosmos," *European Physical Journal H* 40 (March 2015): 301–335, https://arxiv.org/abs/1503.08029.

4. A. Einstein and W. de Sitter, "On the Relation between the Expansion and the Mean Density of the Universe," *Proceedings of the National Academy of Sciences* 18 (1932): 213–214.

5. The authors—although here it is obviously Einstein speaking for himself—justify themselves by writing: "Historically, the term containing the cosmological constant Λ was introduced into the field equations in order to enable us to account theoretically for the existence of a finite mean density in a static universe. It now appears that in the dynamical case this end can be reached without the introduction of Λ."

6. H. P. Robertson, "On the Foundations of Relativistic Cosmology," *Proceedings of the National Academy of Sciences* 15 (1929): 822–829.

7. Otto Heckmann, "Über die Metrik des sich ausdehnenden Universums," *Nachrichten von der Gesellschaft der Wissenschaften zu Göttingen* (1931): 127–130.

8. For details, see S. van den Bergh, "Early History of the Distance Scale Problem," in *The Extragalactic Distance Scale*, eds. M. Livio et al. (Cambridge, UK: Cambridge University Press, 1997).

9. Limits can be set on the earliest possible age of the universe based on the age of the oldest stars in our galaxy and on the abundance of certain radioactive elements. See D. Clayton, "Cosmology, Cosmochronology," in *The Astronomy and Astrophysics Encyclopedia*, ed. S. Maran (New York: Van Nostrand Reinhold, 1992), 153–156.

10. According to the theory of inflation, the universe would have experienced in the first fractions of a second of its evolution a frenetically high rate of expansion, so much so that at the end of this inflationary phase space would have become almost "flat" and would have remained so ever since.

11. "Wilkinson Microwave Anisotropy Probe," NASA, December 22, 2017, http://map.gsfc.nasa.gov/.

12. Adam G. Riess et al., "Observational Evidence from Supernovae for an Accelerating Universe and a Cosmological Constant," *Astronomical Journal* 116, no. 3 (1998): 1009; S. Perlmutter et al., "Discovery of a Supernova Explosion at Half the Age of the Universe," *Nature* 391 (1998): 51.

13. The situation has hardly changed today; it would seem that a publication in *Nature* is a prerequisite for international scientific recognition, regardless of the quality of work published elsewhere.

14. In Odon Godart, "Monseigneur Lemaître, sa vie, son œuvre," *Revue des Questions Scientifique* (1984).

15. Georges Lemaître, "Rencontres avec A. Einstein," *Revue des Questions Scientifiques* 5e série, 19 no. 2 (January 1958): 129–132.

16. And the use remained.

17. In the notes added to O. Godart, "Monseigneur Lemaître, sa vie, son œuvre."

18. As told by the reporter who covered the event. Duncan Aikman, "Lemaître Follows Two Paths to Truth, *New York Times*, February 19, 1933, https://inters.org /files/lemaitre_two_paths_truth_nyt1933.pdf.

19. See Stephanie Lob, "Relatively Unknown: Einstein's Risky 1933 Belgian Stay after Hitler Came to Power," *Times of Israel*, April 28, 2023, https://www.timesofisrael. com/einsteins-risky-1933-belgian-stay-after-hitler-came-to-power/. For more on the danger Einstein faced, see "Einstein's Immigration Papers Found, Displayed," *The History Blog*, May 10, 2011, https://www.thehistoryblog.com/archives/11073.

20. A. Berger, ed., *The Big Bang and Georges Lemaître: Proceedings of a Symposium in Honour of G. Lemaître Fifty Years after His Initiation of Big-Bang Cosmology, Louvain-la-Neuve, Belgium, 10–13 October 1983* (New York: D. Reidel Publishing, 1984), 376–378.

13. BLACK HOLES, FADING SPACE, AND THE STRANGENESS OF THE UNIVERSE (1933–1960)

1. Georges Lemaître, "L'Univers en expansion," *Annales de la Société Scientifique de Bruxelles*, série A, t. III (1933): 51–85. English translation: Georges Lemaître, "The Expanding Universe," trans. M. A. H. MacCallum, *General Relativity and Gravitation* 29, no. 5 (1997): 641–680, http://dx.doi.org/10.1023/A:1018855621348.

2. See J. Eisenstaedt, "Histoire et singularités de la solution de Schwarzschild (1915–1923)," *Archive for History of Exact Sciences* 27, no. 2 (1982): 157–198, https://www.jstor.org/stable/41133669.

3. See Jean-Pierre Luminet, *Black Holes* (Cambridge, UK: Cambridge University Press, 1992).

4. Richard C. Tolman, Proceedings of the National Academy of Sciences 16, no. 4 (1930): 320.

5. With his characteristic sense of humor, Arthur Eddington pooh-poohed the cyclical universe idea in his Gifford Lectures of 1927, saying "I am an Evolutionist, not a Multiplicationist. It seems rather stupid to keep doing the same thing over and over again." *The Nature of the Physical World: The Gifford Lectures 1927* (New York: The Macmillan Company, 1929), 86.

6. The model used by Lemaître for his demonstration is, in today's terminology, a Bianchi type I perfect fluid model.

7. See, for example, S. W. Hawking and G. F. R. Ellis, *The Large Scale Structure of Spacetime* (Cambridge, UK: Cambridge University Press, 1973).

8. The phoenix universe would still find such prestigious advocates as George Gamow, James Peebles, and John Wheeler.

9. Georges Lemaître, "Evolution of the Expanding Universe," *Proceedings of the National Academy of Sciences* 20 (1934): 12–17, https://www.pnas.org/doi/epdf/10.1073/pnas.20.1.12.

10. Y. B. Zel'dovich, "Cosmological Constant and Elementary Particles," *Soviet Physics JETP Letters* 6 (1967): 316–317.

11. See Norbert Straumann, "On the Cosmological Constant Problems and the Astronomical Evidence for a Homogeneous Energy Density with Negative Pressure," *Proceedings du Premier Séminaire Poincaré, Paris* (March 2002), https://www.semanticscholar.org/paper/On-the-Cosmological-Constant-Problems-and-the-for-a-Straumann/45b4e52ec830ffd7679de2fa771eba0516ba331e.

12. Georges Lemaître, "The Strangeness of the Universe," in *Dossier: Georges Lemaître, l'Einstein belge, Revue Générale* no. 2022/3 (de septembre 2022), 47–62, https://pul.uclouvain.be/book/?GCOI=29303100731900.

13. English translation by the present author.

14. The Primeval Atom Hypothesis (1945)

1. Odon Godart was also Lemaître's private secretary. On the life and work of Godart, see René Dejaiffe, "Odon Godart et son œuvre," *Ciel et Terre* 114, no. 4 (1998): 143–148.

2. Although most cosmic rays come not from the primeval atom but from a number of sources such as the sun and other stars, supernovae and their remnants, neutron stars, and black holes, it should be noted that no satisfactory explanation has been given for those that are one hundred billion times more energetic than the others and strike the Earth's atmosphere about once a year. Recent models invoke ultra-energetic cosmic rays coming from the very early universe. If that is true, then Lemaître would not have been totally wrong on this question.

3. See Dominique Lambert, *The Atom of the Universe*, trans. Luc Ampleman (Krakow, Poland: Copernicus Center Press, 2015).

4. "*L'hypothèse de l'atome primitif*," in *Revue des Questions Scientifiques*, 5th series 9 (1948): 321–339; "*L'hypothèse de l'atome primitif*," text of a conference at the Palais de la Découverte, Paris, May 13, 1947, published in Alençon by Poulet-Malassis, 1948.

5. As previously mentioned, the 1945 work is available online in English: Georges Lemaître, *The Primeval Atom: An Essay on Cosmogony*, trans. Betty H. and Serge A. Korff (Canada: D. Van Nostrand Co., 1950), https://archive.org/details/primevalatom0000unse/page/n5/mode/2up.

6. Ferdinand Gonseth was himself the author of books on space and non-euclidean geometries, for example Ferdinand Gonseth, *La géométrie et le problème de l'espace* (Neuchâtel, Switzerland: Editions du Griffon, 1955).

7. E. A. Milne, "A Newtonian Expanding Universe," *The Quarterly Journal of Mathematics* 5, no. 1 (1934): 64–72; E. Milne and W. McCrea, "Newtonian Universes and the Curvature of Space," *The Quarterly Journal of Mathematics* 5, no. 1 (1934): 73–80.

8. E. A. Milne, "A Newtonian Expanding Universe," 64. It is interesting that static models are not possible in Newtonian cosmology without the addition of a term of the same type as the relativistic cosmological constant.

9. H. Bondi and T. Gold, "The Steady State Theory of the Expanding Universe," *Monthly Notices of the Royal Astronomical Society* 108 (1948): 252–270; F. Hoyle, "A New Model for the Expanding Universe," *Monthly Notices of the Royal Astronomical Society* 108 (1948): 372–382.

10. Dominique Lambert, "Religious Interferences at the Origin of Cosmology? The Case of Georges Lemaître," *Forum* 4 (2018): 149–168, https://forum-phil.pusc.it/sites/default/files/pdf/forum-v04-a10.pdf.

11. Lambert, "Religious Interferences"; Giovanni Stein, "Creazione senza Creatore," *Ricerche Astronomiche*, 2/14 (1951): 345–354.

12. Helge Kragh, "What's in a Name: History and Meanings of the Term "Big Bang," Cornell University ArXiv (January 2013), https://arxiv.org/abs/1301.0219.

13. Fred Hoyle, "Continuous Creation," *The Listener*, April 7, 1949, 567-568. The original typescript can be found online at St. John's College, University of Cambridge, http://www.joh.cam.ac.uk/library/special_collections/hoyle/exhibition/radio/.

14. F. Hoyle, *The Nature of the Universe* (Oxford, UK: Blackwell, 1950), 102, 105.

15. GEORGE GAMOW (1904–1968)

1. Edward Teller, "Some Personal Memories about George Gamow," in *Gamow Symposium: ASP Conference Series* 129 (1997): 123, https://articles.adsabs.harvard.edu//full/1997ASPC..129..123T/0000125.000.html.

2. "The Distinguished Life and Career of George Gamow: The Personal and Professional Life of George Gamow," University of Colorado Boulder, Physics [website], accessed March 6, 2024, https://www.colorado.edu/physics/events/outreach/george-gamow-memorial-lecture-series/distinguished-life-and-career-george-gamow.

3. *Mr Tompkins in Wonderland* (1940) was originally published in serial form in *Discovery* magazine (UK) in 1938. Reprinted in *Mr Tompkins in Paperback*, which combines *Mr Tompkins in Wonderland* with *Mr Tompkins Explores the Atom* (Cambridge, UK: Cambridge University Press, 1993).

4. George Gamow, *My World Line: An Informal Autobiography* (New York: Viking Press, 1970), https://archive.org/details/georgegamowmywor0000unse.

16. THE PRIMEVAL SUBSTANCE (1948)

1. Jules Laforgue, "Préludes Autobiographiques" ["Autobiographical Preludes"], *Les Complaintes* (Paris: Leon Vanier, 1885), 10.

2. George Gamow, *The Creation of the Universe* (New York: Viking Press, 1952), 4.

3. As far as I know Gamow never used the term "Big Bang."

4. I follow closely the remarkable review article by Ralph Alpher and Robert Herman, "Early Work on 'Big Bang' Cosmology and Cosmic Blackbody Radiation," in *Modern Cosmology in Retrospect*, eds. B. Bertotti et al. (New York: Cambridge University Press, 1990), 129–157.

5. G. Gamow, "Expanding Universe and the Origin of Chemical Elements," *The Physical Review* 70 (1946): 572.

6. R. Alpher, H. Bethe, and G. Gamow, "The Origin of Chemical Elements," *The Physical Review* 73 (1948): 803.

7. Gamow, *The Creation of the Universe*, 65. Anxious to perpetuate the joke of the article, Gamow purportedly tried to persuade Herman to sign their joint publications under the pseudonym "Delter," but the latter refused.

8. G. Gamow, "The Evolution of the Universe," *Nature* 162 (October 30, 1948): 680–682, https://www.nature.com/articles/162680a0; Ralph Alpher and Robert Herman, "Evolution of the Universe," *Nature* 162 (November 13, 1948): 774–775, https://www.nature.com/articles/162774b0.

9. Gamow, *The Creation of the Universe*, 137–138.

10. Provided in particular by data from the WMAP and Planck satellites, see for example D. Spergel et al., "First Year Wilkinson Microwave Anisotropy Probe (WMAP) Observations: Determination of Cosmological Parameters," *Astrophysical Journal Supplement* 148 (2003): 175; Planck Collaboration, "*Planck 2013 Results. I. Overview of Products and Scientific Results*," Cornell University ArXiv (March 20, 2013), https://arxiv.org/abs/1303.5062.

11. R. Alpher, J. Follin, and R. Herman, "Initial Conditions in the Expanding Universe and Element Synthesis," *The Physical Review* (91) 1953: 479A.

12. See Robert Herman, "Part II: The Prediction of the Cosmic Microwave Background Radiation," *George Gamow Symposium, ASP Conference Series* 129 (1997): 70–83, https://adsabs.harvard.edu/full/1997ASPC..129...70H.

13. F. Hoyle and R. Tayler, "The Mystery of the Cosmic Helium Abundance," *Nature* 203 (1964): 1108.

14. See the review article by R. Wagoner, "Deciphering the Nuclear Ashes of the Early Universe," in *Modern Cosmology in Retrospect*, eds. B. Bertotti et al. (Cambridge, UK: Cambridge University Press, 1990), 159–185.

15. Dominique Lambert, "A Universe from an Atom," *Il Nuovo Saggiatore* 32, nos. 3–4 (2106): 55–66, https://www.ilnuovosaggiatore.sif.it/article/34.

16. R. H. Dicke, P. J. E. Peebles, P. G. Roll, and D. T. Wilkinson, "Cosmic Black Body Radiation," *The Astrophysical Journal* 142 (1965): 414–418; A. Penzias and R. Wilson, "Measurement of Excess Antenna Temperature at 4800 Mc/s," *The Astrophysical Journal* 142 (1965): 419–423.

17. Georges Lemaître, *The Primeval Atom: An Essay on Cosmogony*, trans. Betty H. and Serge A. Korff (Canada: D. Van Nostrand Co., 1950), 78, https://archive.org/details/primevalatom0000unse/page/n5/mode/2up.

18. Private communication, 1996.

19. R. Wilson, "Discovery of the Cosmic Microwave Background," in *Modern Cosmology in Retrospect*, 291–307.

20. R. Alpher, G. Gamow, and R. Herman, "Thermal Cosmic Radiation and the Formation of Protogalaxies," *Proceedings of the National Academy of Sciences* 58 (1967): 2179.

21. S. Weinberg, *The First Three Minutes: A Modern View of the Origin of the Universe* (New York: Basic Books, 1977).

22. R. Alpher and R. Herman, "Big-Bang Cosmology and the Cosmic Black-Body Radiation," *Proceedings of the American Philosophical Society* 199 (1975): 325.

23. In what is known as the "LCDM standard cosmological model," the Hubble-Lemaître parameter (see Chapter 11) is 67.4 ± 0.5 km s^{-1} Mpc^{-1}, the age of the universe (assuming $t = 0$ at the Big Bang) is $(13.787 \pm 0.020) \times 10^9$ years, the age of the universe at the time of emission of the cosmic microwave background was $377,700 \pm 3,200$ years, the critical density parameter corresponding to zero space curvature is $(8.62 \pm 0.12) \times 10^{-27}$ kg/m^3, and the real energy density parameter (including dark matter and dark energy) is 0.9993 ± 0.0019 in units of the critical value.

24. Weinberg, *The First Three Minutes*, ch. 6. To a lesser degree, this attitude persists today among a certain category of experimental physicists.

25. T. Dunham and W. Adams, "New Interstellar Lines in the Ultraviolet Spectrum," *Publications of the American Astronomical Society* 9 (1937): 5.

26. A. McKellar, "Molecular Lines from the Lowest States of the Atomic Molecules Composed of Atoms Probably Present in Interstellar Spaces," *Publications of the Dominion Astrophysical Observatory*, vol. 7 (Victoria, British Columbia: F. A. Acland, 1941), 251–272.

27. Quoted in Ivan Couronne and Issam Ahmed, "Top Cosmologist's Lonely Battle against 'Big Bang' Theory," Phys.org, November 14, 2019, https://phys.org/news /2019-11-cosmologist-lonely-big-theory.html.

17. The Topology of the Universe (1900–present)

1. See, for example, E. Harrison, *Darkness at Night* (Cambridge, MA: Harvard University Press, 1989), and Jean-Pierre Luminet and M. Lachièze-Rey, *De l'infini* (Paris: Dunod, 2019).

2. It is also said to be *trivial*.

3. K. Schwarzschild, "*Ueber das zulaessige Kruemmungsmass des Raumes*," *Vierteljahrschrift d. Astrom. Gesellschaft* 35 (1900): 337. English translation: "On The Permissible Curvature of Space," *Classical and Quantum Gravity* 15 (1998): 2539.

4. Albert Einstein to Willem de Sitter, before March 12, 1917, in *The Collected Papers of Albert Einstein*, vol. 8, *The Berlin Years: Correspondence, 1914–1918* (*English Translation Supplement*), trans. Ann M. Hentschel (Princeton, NJ: Princeton University Press, 1998), document 311, https://einsteinpapers.press.princeton.edu /vol8-trans/330.

5. Though de Sitter says "straight lines," the term usually used in differential geometry is "geodesic." The "straight line" on the surface of a sphere is an arc of a large circle.

6. W. de Sitter, "On Einstein's Theory of Gravitation, and its Astronomical Consequences, Third Paper," *Monthly Notices of the Royal Astronomical Society* 78, no. 1 (November 1917): 3–28, https://articles.adsabs.harvard.edu//full/1917MNRAS ..78....3D/0000003.000.html.

7. A leading expert in geometry and group theory, Weyl held the chair of mathematics at the Zurich Polytechnic Institute—where Einstein had done a mediocre job. "My work has always sought to unite truth and beauty; but when I am forced to make the choice between truth and beauty, I always choose beauty," Weyl later wrote to Freeman Dyson. Quoted in Kenneth Brower, *The Starship and the Canoe* (New York: Bantam, 1971), 21.

8. Albert Einstein to Hermann Weyl, June 31, 1918, in *The Collected Papers of Albert Einstein*, vol. 8, document 551, https://einsteinpapers.press.princeton.edu/vol8 -trans/598. Emphasis in original.

9. No one was more qualified than Felix Klein to discuss the topology of space: in 1872, at the age of only 23, he presented a dissertation on geometry for the new academic year at the University of Erlangen, which contained the seeds of a curriculum designed to bring together the geometric disciplines that had been dispersed until then. This was a major moment in the history of mathematics, at the origin of

the integration of geometry into a unified view of mathematics based on symmetry, groups of transformations, and topology.

10. Einstein is alluding to the hypertorus, a variant of the three-dimensional euclidean space obtained by considering as identical all the points belonging to the opposite sides of a parallelepiped. See Jean-Pierre Luminet, *L'Univers chiffonné* (Paris: Fayard, 2001); English translation: Jean-Pierre Luminet, *The Wraparound Universe*, trans. Eric Novak (Wellesley, MA: A. K. Peters, 2008). For more technical details, see M. Lachièze-Rey and J.-P. Luminet, "Cosmic Topology," *Physics Reports* 254 (1995): 135–214.

11. Albert Einstein to Felix Klein, April 16, 1919, in *The Collected Papers of Albert Einstein*, vol. 9, *The Berlin Years: Correspondence, January 1919–April 1920* (English Translation Supplement), trans. Ann M. Hentschel (Princeton, NJ: Princeton University Press, 1998), document 24, https://einsteinpapers.press.princeton.edu /vol9-trans/41.

12. Luminet, *The Wraparound Universe*.

13. E. Fedorov, "Symmetry of Regular Systems of Figures," in *Russian Journal for Crystallography and Mineralogy*, vol. 21 (Saint-Pétersbourg, 1885); L. Bieberbach, "On the Groups of Motions of euclidean Spaces I," *Mathematische Annalen* 70 (1911): 297–336; and II, *Mathematische Annalen* 72 (1912): 400–412.

14. W. Nowacki, "The euclidean, Three-Dimensional, Closed and Open Space Forms," *Commentarii Mathematici Helvetici* 7 (1934): 81–93.

15. F. Klein, "Zur nicht-euklidischen Geometrie," *Mathematisches Annalen* 37 (1890): 544; W. Killing, "Über die Clifford-Kleinschen Raumformen," *Mathematisches Annalen* 39 (1891): 257.

16. W. Threlfall and H. Seifert, "Topologische Untersuchung der Diskontinuitätsbereiche endlicher Bewegungsgruppen des dreidimensionalen sphärischen Raumes, *Mathematische Annalen* 104 (1930): 1–70 and "Topologische Untersuchung der Diskontinuitätsbereiche endlicher Bewegungsgruppen des dreidimensionalen sphärischen Raumes," *Mathematische Annalen* 107 (1932): 543–586. See also J. A. Wolf, "Sur la classification des variétés riemanniennes homogènes à courbure constante," *Comptes rendus de l'Académie des Sciences de Paris* 250 (1960) 3443–3445.

17. E. Gausmann, R. Lehoucq, J.-P. Luminet, J.-P. Uzan, and J. Weeks, "Topological Lensing in Elliptical Spaces," *Classical and Quantum Gravity* 18 (2001): 5155–5186.

18. A brilliant synthesis is presented in W. Thurston, *Three-Dimensional Geometry and Topology* (Princeton, NJ: Princeton University Press, 1997). In 1982 Thurston was awarded the Fields Medal, the equivalent in mathematics of a Nobel Prize.

19. Jeffrey R. Weeks, *The Shape of Space*, 3rd edition (New York: CRC Press, 2020).

20. I would say, more precisely, it is about the larger problem of the topology of the universe, on which the question of the finite or infinite extension of space depends. Since Friedmann's ironic remark, the situation has hardly changed: many books on cosmology that are today "references" evade the real topological question or repeat mathematically "unfounded" assertions; this is notably the case in an otherwise exceptional work, S. Weinberg's *Gravitation and Cosmology* (New York: Wiley, 1972) section 14.2.

21. To clarify Friedmann's statement: this condition is equivalent to saying that space is simply connected. Otherwise, the space is multiconnected.

22. The topological variants of the spaces are in fact obtained by identification between points in the space. The cylinder given as an example by Friedmann is obtained from the euclidean plane by identifying point by point two parallel straight lines. The mathematical and cosmological aspects of the question are developed in M. Lachièze-Rey and J.-P. Luminet, "Cosmic Topology," and in Luminet, *The Wraparound Universe*.

23. However, we can say that all spaces with positive curvature are finite.

24. Translated by the author. Original Russian edition, Alexander A. Friedmann, *Mir kak prostranstvo i vremya*, 1923. French translation by A. Grib and the present author in Jean-Pierre Luminet, *Alexandre Friedmann, Georges Lemaître: Essais de Cosmologie* (Paris: Le Seuil, 1997). For another English translation, see *The Word as Space and Time*, trans. Svetla Kirilova-Petkova and Vesselin Petkov (Montreal: Minkowski Institute Press, 2014), 80–81.

25. For more on the philosophical underpinnings of Lemaître's discoveries, see Dominique Lambert, "Was the Big Bang Theory Born out of Belief? Lemaître's Primeval Atom Hypothesis," *Dialogue: Theologie & Naturwissenschaften*, September, 2017, https://www.theologie-naturwissenschaften.de/en/dialogue-between -theology-and-science/editorials/big-bang.

26. Georges Lemaître, "The Primeval Atom Hypothesis and the Problem of the Clusters of Galaxies," in *La structure et l'évolution de l'univers. Rapports et discussions.* Eleventh Council of Solvay Physics (Bruxelles: R. Stoops, 1958), 7.

27. The text of Lemaître's Institut Catholique de Paris lecture was published post-humously in "L'Univers, problème accessible à la science humaine," *Revue d'Histoire Scientifique* 31 (1978): 345–359.

28. Lemaître, "The Primeval Atom Hypothesis and the Problem of the Clusters of Galaxies," 3.

29. Weinberg, *Gravitation and Cosmology*; George Gamow, *The Creation of the Universe* (New York: Viking Press, 1952).

30. G. Ellis, "Topology and Cosmology," *General Relativity and Gravitation*, vol. 2, 1971, 7–21.

31. All references to these pioneering works can be found in Lachièze-Rey and Luminet, "Cosmic Topology."

32. Lachièze-Rey and Luminet, "Cosmic Topology."

33. Developed notably in R. Lehoucq, M. Lachièze-Rey. and J.-P. Luminet, "Cosmic Crystallography," *Astronomy and Astrophysics* 313 (1996): 339–346.

34. J.-P. Luminet, J. Weeks, A. Riazuelo, R. Lehoucq, and J.-P. Uzan, "Dodecahedral Space Topology as an Explanation for Weak Wide-Angle Temperature Correlations in the Cosmic Microwave Background," *Nature* 425 (October 9, 2003): 593–595; Ralf Aurich et al., "Do We Live in a 'Small Universe'?," *Classical and Quantum Gravity* 25, no. 12 (2008): 125006.

35. Luminet, *The Wraparound Universe*, Chapter 14.

36. Planck Collaboration, "Planck 2013 Results. XXVI. Background Geometry and Topology of the Universe," Cornell University ArXiv (2013), https://arxiv.org/abs /1303.5086.

37. Jean-Pierre Luminet, "Cosmic Topology," *Scholarpedia* 10, no. 8 (2015): 31544.

18. CONCLUSION

1. Not all of them have been discussed in this book.

2. W. McCrea, "Personal Recollections: Some Lessons for the Future," in *Modern Cosmology in Retrospect*, eds. B. Bertotti et al. (Cambridge, UK: Cambridge University Press, 1990), 197–220.

APPENDIX 3. CORRESPONDENCE BETWEEN LEMAÎTRE AND EINSTEIN (1947)

1. In English, in the Lemaître Archives, Archives de l'Université catholique de Louvain.

2. Paul Arthur Schilpp, ed., *Albert Einstein: Philosopher-Scientist* (Evanston, IL: Northwestern University Press, 1949), in the collection "The Library of Living Philosophers." The volume was published on the occasion of Einstein's seventieth birthday, with Einstein himself contributing a text in German accompanied by an English translation, entitled "Autobiographisches—Autobiographical Notes."

3. In English, in the Lemaître Archives, Archives de l'Université catholique de Louvain.

4. This is a profound remark by Lemaître, based on an idea by Eddington who had already interpreted λ in quantum terms. The cosmological constant appears, today, as a necessity of the quantum theory, linked to the minimal level of energy (the energy of the vacuum).

5. It should be noted that Lemaître sometimes uses the expression "cosmic constant," and sometimes the expression "cosmological constant."

6. Lemaître alludes here to the fact that due to the existence of positive and negative electric charges, the effects of the electric field quickly neutralize themselves with the distance and the amount of material involved.

CREDITS

Figure 1.1. Hubble smoking a pipe. "Studio portrait photograph of Edwin Powell Hubble." Photograph by Johan Hagemeyer, Camera Portraits Carmel, 1931, Wikimedia Commons. Public domain.

Figure 2.1. Young Einstein. "Einstein patent office." Photograph by Lucien Chavan, 1904 or 1905, Wikimedia Commons. Public domain.

Figure 3.1. Einstein lecturing. "Albert Einstein 1921." Photograph by F. Schmutzer, 1921, Wikimedia Commons. Public domain.

Figure 3.2. Einstein's "cylindrical" universe, by Jean-Pierre Luminet.

Figure 3.3. Willem DeSitter. "WillemDeSitter3." Photographer unknown, Wide World Photos, date unknown, Wikimedia Commons. Public domain.

Figure 4.1. Friedmann. "Fridman AA." Photographer unknown, 1916, Wikimedia Commons. Public domain.

Figure 5.1. Three simple graphs by Jean-Pierre Luminet.

Figure 8.1. Brothers Georges and Jacques Lemaître. "Lemaître 1914." Photographer unknown, 1914, Wikimedia Commons. Public domain.

Figure 8.2. De Sitter, Einstein, and others. "Einstein, Ehrenfest & De Sitter; Eddington & Lorentz. Location: office of W. de Sitter in Leiden (The Netherlands)." Photograph by H. van Batenburg, September 26, 1923, Wikimedia Commons. CCA-SA 3.0 license.

Figure 9.1. Georges Lemaître in Canada. Photographer unknown, 1925, Archives de l'Université catholique de Louvain: Archives Georges Lemaître, BE A4006 FG LEM-314. CCA-NC-ND 4.0 International license.

Figure 9.2. Lemaître's 1927 universe model. Graph recreated by Jean-Pierre Luminet.

Figure 9.3. Handwritten graph by Georges Lemaître, 1927. Archives de l'Université catholique de Louvain: Archives Georges Lemaître, BE A4006 FG LEM.

Figure 9.4. Arthur Eddington. "Portrait of Arthur Stanley Eddington (1882-1944), Astronomer." Photograph by Transocean, date prior to 1944, Smithsonian Institution Libraries.

Figure 9.5. Two graphs, one based on Lemaître's 1927 data and the other from a 1929 article by Hubble. See the endnote for the Figure 9.5 caption for credit/source information.

Figure 10.1. Manuscript version of Lemaître's 1931 article for *Nature*, with an interesting sentence crossed out by Lemaître himself. Archives de l'Université catholique de Louvain: Archives Georges Lemaître, BE A4006 FG LEM.

Figure 11.1. Lemaître's "hesitating universe," by Jean-Pierre Luminet.

Figure 12.1. Einstein and Lemaître in the street, Pasadena, CA, January 1932. AP. Photographer unknown.

Figure 15.1. George Gamow. "Informal Portrait of Gamow." Photographer unknown, date unknown, American Institute of Physics, Emilio Segrè Visual Archives, Gamow George B13.

Figure 17.1. WMAP satellite (artist's conception). "WMAP Spacecraft: WMAP Heading for L2." Image by NASA / WMAP Science Team, #990387, March 30, 2017. Public domain.

Figure A1.1 Cosmological constant, by Jean-Pierre Luminet.

Figure A2.1. Histogram giving the number of cosmology articles published between 1932 and 1972—graph by Jean-Pierre Luminet.

INDEX

Made in the USA
Las Vegas, NV
02 May 2024

89431721R00152